CIVIL ENGINEERING

West Midlands

Essex Bridge, Great Haywood.

CIVIL ENGINEERING HERITAGE

West Midlands

Roger Cragg

PHILLIMORE

2010
Phillimore & Co. Ltd.
Andover, Hampshire, England

© Roger Cragg, 2010

ISBN 978-1-86077-572-7

ALSO IN THE CIVIL ENGINEERING HERITAGE SERIES
(General Editor: Peter Cross-Rudkin)

East Anglia by Peter Cross-Rudkin

Wales by Keith Thomas

CONTENTS

Britain has a heritage of civil engineering structures and works unrivalled anywhere else. The skills of past engineers are in evidence throughout the land in a fascinating variety of bridges, structures, utilities and lines of communication: the infrastructure of society.

The series *Civil Engineering Heritage* makes available information about these works to a wide public in order to broaden the interest and understanding of the reader in the immense range of expertise that features in our history. In recent years people have become more aware of the value of our heritage and our responsibility to keep the best examples for future generations. It is therefore hoped that these books will assist those seeking to advance the cause of conservation.

Much of the information in these books, particularly in the Gazetteer, has been extracted from the records of civil engineering works prepared by the Institution of Civil Engineers' Panel for Historical Engineering Works (PHEW). The works covered by these records have been selected for their technical interest, innovation, association with eminent engineers or contractors, rarity or visual attraction. The Institution's Archives have become the principal national repository for records of civil engineering and are now regarded as the leading authority on historical engineering works. They are widely consulted by heritage organisations, the business community and those involved in private research. The records may be consulted by the public for research purposes on application to the Institution's Archivist. The relevant Historical Engineering Work number is given, where one exists, for each item in the Gazetteer to assist researchers in following up items of interest. Additionally, PHEW has a number of subpanels dealing with specific types of civil engineering works in greater detail, who are able to assist with information about works within their remit.

The author would like to thank the following members of PHEW for their assistance in the preparation of this volume: Dr Barry Barton, Peter Cross-Rudkin, Keith Thomas and the late Paul Dunkerley. The valuable assistance of Mike Chrimes, Head of Knowledge Transfer at the Institution of Civil Engineers, and his staff in providing illustrations and information is acknowledged. Thanks are due to the following individuals who have assisted in the preparation of the volume and also those who, over many years, have made a major contribution towards gathering the information upon which this book has been based: Richard Martin, John Bonnett, Col. A.P.DeT. Daniell and Philip Shaw.

Thanks are also due to the numerous record offices, local authorities, public utilities and others, too numerous to mention, who have helped PHEW with their enquiries over the years.

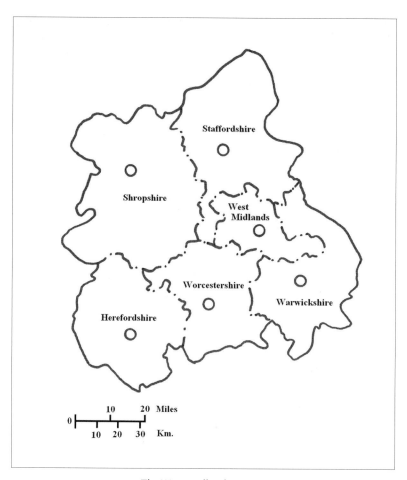

The West Midlands region.

Over the last 300 years, British civil engineers have been prominent in the design and construction of the infrastructure which has so transformed the lives of the population not only of this country but all over the world. In particular they have been noteworthy in the provision of transport facilities, with the development of roads, inland waterways and canals, railways, docks and harbours and, more recently, airports; in the provision of water supply, drainage and sewage treatment, and the provision of power supply for homes and industry from water, wind and fossil fuels. Within the pages of this book will be found many examples of the skills of the civil engineer which illustrate this wide range of activity.

This volume in the Civil Engineering Heritage series covers the West Midlands region, which includes the counties of Herefordshire, Shropshire, Staffordshire, Warwickshire, West Midlands and Worcestershire. The book is designed to be of interest to the general reader as well as to those with an engineering background and is structured in two main parts. The first five chapters cover bridges, inland waterways, railways, roads and public utilities and power. The second section is a Gazetteer which contains details of over 175 sites arranged by county, nearly all of which can be visited or viewed from nearby. The national grid reference is given for each site and, where the location is not obvious from the description, information is given on access to the site. In the few cases where the sites are not accessible to the public they are illustrated and have been included as they have an important place in the heritage of civil engineering in the region. Most of the sites and structures are illustrated. Sites printed in **bold** characters in the chapters are sites which can be found in the Gazetteer.

The character of the West Midlands region is diverse, varying from the intensively industrialised area of the aptly named Black Country to the rural aspects of Herefordshire and Worcestershire. Over the last 300 years the appearance of the region's counties has changed.

Although now regarded as being predominantly rural, Shropshire was, for a relatively short period of time, one of the cradles of the Industrial Revolution. Along the gorge of the River Severn at Coalbrookdale was found the necessary combination of raw materials (coal and iron ore), transport (the river) and the inventiveness of Abraham Darby and his successors which led to the development of the historic iron founding industry there. Later, following the opening of the eponymous structure, the area became known as Ironbridge.

Staffordshire also exhibits marked contrasts between the potteries of the five towns of Stoke-on-Trent with the nearby moorlands to the north and Cannock Chase in the south of the county. Through Staffordshire pass some of the important transport routes of the region, including the Trent & Mersey Canal, the Grand Junction Railway and, more recently, the M6 motorway. Thomas Brassey, probably the best known of the Victorian contractors, started his railway building career in the county with the building of Penkridge Viaduct on the Grand Junction Railway.

Warwickshire, having in 1974 lost the area including Coventry and Birmingham, now part of the West Midlands county, has become a predominantly rural county. There is some industrial activity in the north around Nuneaton and Rugby and in the south, the tourist magnet of Stratford-upon-Avon and the north Cotswolds. As with Staffordshire above, the county is crossed by some of the oldest and newest transport routes including the Coventry and Stratford-upon-Avon canals, the London & Birmingham Railway, one of the earliest long distance railway routes, Thomas Telford's Holyhead Road and the M45 and M6 motorways.

As mentioned above, the county of West Midlands is almost totally industrialised, from Coventry, cradle of the bicycle and motor car industries, in the east, through Birmingham, with its multitude of trades, to Wolverhampton in the west. Partly because of a lack of navigable rivers in the area, the development of the canal system here was unsurpassed anywhere in the world. Much early railway development also took place here and Birmingham was the target for two of the earliest railway schemes, the Grand Junction and the London & Birmingham, recognising its rapidly growing importance in the 19th century. Today much of the old heavy industry has been replaced by new developments but enough remains to remind us of its past industrial glories.

Herefordshire and Worcestershire, from 1974 amalgamated into one county but now separated again, have similar characteristics. They were not greatly affected by the Industrial Revolution which so greatly altered the area to the north and east. Consequently the main towns such as Hereford, Evesham and Worcester still perform their ancient functions as commercial centres in a predominantly rural area. Communications were dominated from earliest times by the River Severn, together with the River Avon, the only major rivers in the region. Development of the industrial Midlands on the higher ground to the north-east required new links to the river in the form of the Staffordshire & Worcestershire Canal in 1772 and later the Worcester & Birmingham Canal in 1815. After the canals came the railways, with the Birmingham & Gloucester in 1840 and, in more recent times, the M5 motorway.

Within the pages that follow will be found the names of engineers familiar to many readers – Thomas Telford, James Brindley, Robert Stephenson and others. However, the reader will also find the names (and some biographical information) of less well-known engineers, all of whom made their contribution to the development of civil engineering, and also the names of many of the contractors who undertook the building of the works described. In the past their involvement has often received less credit than is their due.

In presenting this volume it is hoped that all readers, both those with an engineering background and the more general reader, will further their understanding of the contribution made by civil engineers to the economic and social development of the West Midlands region.

Roger Cragg
Coventry, November 2009

Imperial measurements have been generally adopted for the dimensions of the works described in this book as this would have been the system used at the time of the design and construction of most of them. Where modern structures have been included which were designed and built using the metric system, metric units have been used in the text.

The following are the metric equivalents of the imperial units used:

Length:	1 inch = 25.4 millimetres
	1 foot = 0.3048 metres
	1 yard = 0.9144 metres
	1 mile = 1.609 kilometres
Area:	1 square inch = 45.2 square millimetres
	1 square foot = .0929 square metres
	1 acre = 0.4047 hectares
	1 square mile = 259 hectares
Volume:	1 gallon = 4.546 litres
	1 million gallons = 4546 cubic metres
	1 cubic yard = 0.7646 cubic metres
Mass:	1 pound = 0.4536 kilograms
	1 ton = 1.016 tonnes
Power:	1 horsepower (h.p.) = 0.7457 kilowatts
Pressure:	1 pound force per square inch = 0.06895 bar

1   *Bridge 131A, Oxford Canal.*

2   *Pointed and semi-circular arches, Tidmington Packhorse Bridge.*

There are currently thought to be about 75,000 bridges in Great Britain and this chapter considers the history and development of bridges in the West Midlands. The development of bridge design has been mainly influenced by developments in two of its aspects. The introduction over the years of new materials has allowed designers to modify the form of bridges. Thus the introduction of cast iron as a bridge building material in the late 18th century enabled designers such as Thomas Telford to produce arch bridge designs which were lighter and of greater spans than was possible with earlier designs in timber or with masonry arches. Similarly the development in the 20th century of reinforced concrete and, later, prestressed concrete led to the new designs of bridges with which we are now familiar. However, it must be borne in mind that these changes in materials and design were not sudden and older types continued to be designed and built alongside the newer designs for some years. At the end of the chapter some more specialised types of bridges, including suspension and moveable bridges and canal aqueducts, will be considered.

Bridges have been used by man from the very earliest times and no doubt the first bridge was a large log which had conveniently fallen across a stream which enabled an early human to cross without getting his feet wet. It is a very small step from that to the deliberate cutting down and placing of a tree across a stream at a place where it was more convenient. A footbridge over the Oxford Canal near Fenny Compton is one almost as simple, consisting of a single baulk of timber supported on timber trestle supports. It was built in 1907 and survived until recently but has now been demolished. Unfortunately, given the nature of the material, not many of these timber bridges have survived the passage of time, but there is a rather unusual 'hybrid' bridge, **Whitney Toll Bridge (HE12)**, across the River Wye at Whitney, near Hay-on-Wye, which was built in about 1820. The bridge has stone arches leading from both banks and a central section in timber. The bridge is also unusual in remaining a toll bridge. Many years ago a large number of bridges charged tolls but, apart from a small number of large modern bridges, most tolls were bought out from the previous private owners by highway and bridge authorities.

The Romans seem to have used timber superstructures on timber or stone abutments and piers, although it is now believed that a small number of major bridges had stone arches. There was then a hiatus for about four hundred years until from the eighth century the Anglo-Saxons began again to build new bridges, whose existence is known mainly from reference in charters. From the 11th century bridges generally had stone arches, although from the 15th century some were built of brick; only a few hundred masonry ones retain all or part of their medieval fabric.

Ascribing dates to bridges built before the middle of the 18th century is difficult to do with any degree of certainty, because of the lack of contemporary records. Even where accounts do exist, the present structure may be a subsequent rebuilding that has passed unrecorded. It is necessary therefore to look at the structure itself. Unfortunately there is no clear transition from one style to the other as in, say, church architecture. Some clues may be found in the arch shape. The earliest were either semi-circular, in the Romanesque tradition, or curved-pointed Gothic arches. A small packhorse bridge near Tidmington (SP 245376), south of Shipston on Stour in Warwickshire, dating from 1615 and a Scheduled Ancient Monument, has two arches, one pointed and one semi-circular. Similarly, **Stare Bridge (WK30)** in Warwickshire, which dates from the 14th century, has a number of pointed arches. Of semi-circular arch bridges there are many excellent examples in the area extending over a long period of time, from the 18th-century bridge at Barford over the River Avon in Warwickshire, with its five brick and stone arches, to the fine bridge at Bredwardine, over the River Wye, with six brick arches. **Bredwardine Bridge (HE1)** illustrates one of the disadvantages of the semi-circular arch since the height of its 32ft-span arches is 16ft, thus making the approach to the bridge from the low south bank of the river rather steep.

It is commonly supposed that medieval bridges were narrow, suitable only for the passage of packhorse traffic. In fact, by the end of the medieval period most bridges on major routes and over major rivers were wide enough for carts, with a median width of about 12ft. Most bridges now broader than this have been widened at some stage. Where the widening has been done to one side the elevations may be different, but often both sides were extended and it is necessary to look underneath, where the join is usually visible. **Water Orton Bridge (WM28)** is noteworthy as, unlike nearly all the other medieval bridges in the area, it has not been widened and today is only able to carry a single file of modern traffic. The similarly dated bridge **Coleshill Bridge (WK4)** illustrates the effects of widening – the west elevation being the original stone bridge with a width of 12ft 9in while the east elevation was widened in brick by a further 5ft 4in in 1900.

3 *Bredwardine Bridge, River Wye.*

From the 14th century segmental arches (being the segment of a circle less than a semi-circle and usually about 120 degrees) enabled the construction of a flatter profile and therefore less steep approaches, important when motive power was provided by horses. Shuttington Bridge (SK 249051), on the Staffordshire/Warwickshire boundary near Tamworth, illustrates the two types of arch. The older section of the bridge has three pointed arches of spans ranging from 11 to 15 feet, but the northern section of the bridge, rebuilt in 1816, has two segmental brick arches having approximately the same rise as the pointed arches but which allow larger spans of between 27 and 30 feet. An extreme example of this type of arch is James Brindley's very flat segmental arch bridge at Great Haywood in Staffordshire, which carries the towpath of the Trent &

4 *Telford's Montford Bridge, built in 1792.*

Mersey Canal over the entrance to the Staffordshire & Worcestershire Canal. The arch of **Great Haywood Canal Bridge (ST15)**, with a span of 35ft 6in, has a rise of only about six feet. The equivalent semi-circular arch would have had a rise of over 17ft, making the approach ramps impossibly steep for the canal horses.

Another development that may help to provide a rough date for a bridge is the ratio of the width of the piers (along the line of the bridge) to the span of the arches. As time progressed the piers became relatively more slender. Span lengths in themselves give few clues to the age of a bridge. Most medieval bridges in the Midlands do not exceed 20ft in any arch and the largest in the region, the **Wye Bridge (HE5)** in Hereford, built in 1490, reaches 36ft.

There are many examples of semi-circular and segmental arch bridges in the West Midlands and it is only possible to select a few of the more outstanding examples to illustrate this aspect of bridge design. These bridges were the work of many fine engineers and among the most prominent was Thomas Telford who had a long association with canal, road and bridge works in the West Midlands.

Thomas Telford, born in Eskdale in the Scottish Borders, the son of a shepherd, was trained as a stonemason. Having moved to London in 1782 he worked on the building of Somerset House but soon moved to Portsmouth, supervising work on the new dockyard buildings. In 1787 he moved to Shrewsbury to oversee work on the castle and later that year was appointed Surveyor of Public Works for the County of Shropshire. In this capacity he was responsible for the design of many bridges in the county.

The first bridge to be designed and built by Telford for the county was **Montford Bridge (SH21)** with three segmental arches in the local red sandstone, which opened on Lady Day 1792 and, until recently, carried Telford's Holyhead Road over the River Severn west of Shrewsbury. It was widened in 1963 and has now been by-passed by a new section of the A5 road. It still carries local traffic and bears a plaque unveiled by the President of the Institution of Civil Engineers in 2007 commemorating the 250th anniversary of the birth of Telford in 1757 and his election as the first President of the Institution of Civil Engineers in 1820. Subsequently Thomas Telford became the pre-eminent civil engineer of his time and, in a long career, carried out numerous works in the West Midlands. We shall meet him again in the chapters on canals and roads.

Other engineers who were responsible for bridges in the region include Joseph Potter of Lichfield, who became in 1801 the Surveyor of County Bridges for Staffordshire. One of his responsibilities was the completion of **Wolseley Bridge (ST7)**, which was designed by John Rennie, following difficulties with the original contractor. Potter also was responsible, with his youngest son James, for the design of **Chetwynd Bridge (ST1)** with three large cast-iron arches. In Herefordshire John Gethin, a stonemason and the County Surveyor, was responsible for the building of a large number of masonry arch bridges in the county, many of which are still carrying modern traffic. An excellent example of John Gethin's work is **Burrington Bridge (HE8)** of 1813 over the River Teme. Two characteristics of Gethin's bridges, seen at Burrington, are firstly the recessing of the arch and spandrels to form a rectangular frame around the arch, and secondly the provision of circular holes in the spandrels, reducing the weight of the bridge. There are many examples of bridges by Gethin in Herefordshire, some of which are listed in the Gazetteer.

Elliptical arches were introduced to Britain in the 1760s after a fierce architectural debate about the aesthetics of the proposed Blackfriars Bridge in London. The **Tramway Bridge (WK34)** over the River Avon at Stratford-upon-Avon, which formerly carried the track of the Stratford & Moreton Tramway and dates from 1825, has nine semi-elliptical arches in red brick. The designer was John Urpeth Rastrick. Rastrick was one of the most important engineers of his generation and, following work at Ketley Foundry in Shropshire, was Engineer at Bridgnorth Foundry but left there in 1817. In 1819 he became Managing Partner in the firm of Foster, Rastrick & Partners at Stourbridge. Among the products of the foundry were the Agenoria and Stourbridge Lion steam locomotives and Rastrick was closely involved with many early railway and tramway schemes, including the Stratford & Moreton line which will be referred to further in Chapter 3.

An advantage of the semi-elliptical arch is that it gives a greater headroom at the ends of the arch when compared with the equivalent segmental arch. This was taken advantage of by the designers of a large number of cast-iron towpath bridges on the Birmingham canal network and elsewhere since it gave a greater headroom for the canal horses walking along the towpath. The bridge illustrated (SP 326789) was originally sited on the Oxford Canal north of Coventry but was displaced during the construction of the M6 motorway. The bridge was re-sited on a housing development in the City and is a good example of the preservation of a structure by re-use on another site.

Another feature, usually of older bridges, and best seen from below, is the ribbed arch where narrow separate ribs of ashlar take the place of the normal arch vault. There are about 125 of these remaining in England. They date mostly from the 13th to the 15th centuries, although some continued to be built until the 17th century. It is not clear why the masons chose to use this form; the standard of stonework needed to be high. In some cases the stones above span between the ribs, effectively giving two arch rings, but in others they do not and would have required centering for their support

5 *Burrington Bridge, designed by John Gethin, 1813.*

6 *Preserved towpath bridge, Oxford Canal, Spon End, Coventry.*

7 *Ribbed arch, Stoneleigh Bridge.*

during construction. There are several examples in the area covered by this volume although some are difficult to see. Two examples may be quoted. The first is **Stoneleigh Bridge (WK31)** in Warwickshire, which, although widened, has three deep ribs in one of its eight segmental arches. A second example is **Furnace End Bridge (WK12)**, in Warwickshire over the Bourne Brook, which has four ribs, but these are difficult to see since the bridge was widened in 1924. There are also traces of earlier ribbed arches on the **Wye Bridge (HE5)** at Hereford previously mentioned.

Almost one half of the masonry bridges in Britain were canal and railway over- and under-bridges. This led to the production of standard bridge designs by consulting engineers who were based away from the construction sites, which would be adapted by the resident engineers to suit the individual locations.

From the 1770s onwards there was an increasing use in bridge construction of a new material, cast iron. From the first 30 years, up to 1810, only 14 bridges survive, including three aqueducts. After the Iron Bridge (see below), the most interesting is the one built in 1803 at Culford, Suffolk to Samuel Wyatt's patent, which proved like most of the others to be a technical cul-de-sac. The West Midlands is fortunate in being the location for several of the earliest cast-iron bridges, including the first in the world at Ironbridge, previously known as Coalbrookdale. This was the location of the iron foundry of Abraham Darby III and he was a major promoter of the new bridge, completed in 1779. **The Iron Bridge (SH16)**, now free of road traffic and preserved, spans 100ft 6in across the River Severn and is notable in being largely constructed using mortice and tenon joints and wedges, an example of building in a new material in a style more suited to an earlier material, in this case timber. Just a short distance downstream from the Iron Bridge is **Coalport Bridge (SH11)**, only a few years younger than its more famous cousin. The bridge has a long history and was originally a wooden bridge dating from 1780, the timber deck of which was rebuilt on three iron ribs in 1799. In 1818 it was widened and an iron superstructure added to give its present configuration. It has a slightly longer span at 103ft. It has the distinction of being the oldest iron bridge still carrying vehicular traffic, albeit severely weight restricted. It has recently undergone an extensive refurbishment. From 1811 a number of designs emerged that used cast iron to its best effect, in various configurations of arches. These included two different types by Thomas Telford and William Hazledine at Meole Brace, Shrewsbury, and Bonar Bridge in Scotland, both now demolished; by John Rennie and the Butterley Company over the fen drains at Boston; and the designs, presumably in-house, of Yorkshire foundries such as Aydon & Elwell. Although Meole Brace bridge did not survive, there is a smaller example in south Shropshire at **Cantlop (SH9)**. The bridge, now by-passed, has four cast-iron ribs of 32ft span formed from two halves with a joint at the crown of the arch.

William Hazledine was an important figure in iron bridge construction in the West Midlands. From his successive foundries at Shrewsbury and Plas Kynaston near Ruabon there emerged castings for many of the iron bridges in the region. He was particularly associated with the works of Thomas Telford in the area and provided castings for the Menai and Conwy suspension bridges and Chirk and Pontcysyllte aqueducts as well as several iron bridges in Shropshire and over the River Severn.

8   Detail of arch at Cantlop Bridge, designed by Thomas Telford, 1812.

The early cast-iron bridges often attempted to emulate the forms of timber or masonry. Cast iron is relatively weak in tension and therefore not ideal for horizontal beams in which considerable tensile stresses occur at the bottom of the beam that may lead to sudden fracture, but it is excellent in arches where the material is in a constant state of compression. Within the area covered by this volume there are many fine

9   Galton Bridge, designed by Thomas Telford, 1829.

examples of cast-iron arch bridges, some of considerable span. The earliest have already been mentioned but later designers recognised the advantages of the new material, the arches of the larger span bridges being made up from smaller segments bolted together. Thomas Telford was a particular exponent of this technique and developed a standard design for his 150ft span bridges. Two examples of this type of bridge exist in the West Midlands, **Galton Bridge (WM23)** of 1829 over Telford's massive Smethwick cutting with the roadway about 65ft above the Birmingham Canal, and one year earlier **Holt Fleet Bridge (WR9)** in Worcestershire over the River Severn. Both bridges have a span of 150ft and the abutments of Galton Bridge are founded well up the sides of the cutting, a bold move which saved much masonry work. The bridge at Holt Fleet was stiffened in 1927 by casting reinforced concrete slabs to encase the lower and upper flanges of the arch ribs.

It was the research of Eaton Hodgkinson from 1827 and the collaboration of William Fairbairn that led to an understanding of the proper proportions for cast-iron beams. The manufacturing process was not entirely reliable, occasionally giving rise to unexpected brittleness or voids in the structure and, although longer lengths were sometimes used, most engineers limited themselves to 30ft spans. Later, failures on the Chester & Holyhead Railway, the London & Croydon Railway and the Great North of Scotland Railway led to a ban on the use of cast iron for railway underbridges and probably one of the last uses of cast iron for the main structure of a bridge was in 1906. It will sometimes be observed that the outer beam of a railway underbridge remains as a cast-iron beam but it will usually be found that the main structure has been replaced by a steel beam bridge and the outer cast-iron beam retained merely to support the parapet of the bridge.

Wrought iron offered many of the advantages of cast iron with the additional one of being strong in tension as well as in compression. Until James Neilson patented his hot blast method of manufacture in 1828, the cost of the product prevented its use for bridgework, but in 1831 a girder bridge of moderate span was built over a railway in Glasgow. Of greater significance was the development of a number of truss types that could use wrought iron (and sometimes cast iron where it was possible to know that certain truss members would always be in compression) to provide economical spans up to 250ft. A remarkable wrought-iron truss bridge can be found over the disused London & North Western Railway line between Leamington Spa and Rugby situated on a farm track to the south of Hunningham in Warwickshire. **Hunningham Railway Bridge (WK17)** was completed in 1850 and originally, with a single span of 150ft, was briefly the longest wrought-iron truss bridge in the world. However, its stability has at some time been called into question and it will be observed today that the span has been propped at its third points, thus converting the single 150ft span into three 50ft spans. The designer of this bridge was William Doyne, working for the line's Engineer, Robert Stephenson.

Steel replaced wrought iron for some uses from the 1850s but some well-reported failures in ships convinced the authorities to ban its use in bridges until the 1880s. The Forth Railway Bridge, opened in 1890, was built of steel and demonstrated convinc-ingly that the problems had been overcome, and thereafter wrought iron was almost entirely superseded. Steel bridges are almost too numerous to warrant special mention but two slightly less usual bridges may be mentioned. The first is **Foregate Street railway bridge (WR15)** in Worcester, a single-span steel plate girder bridge which carries the Worcester to Malvern railway line over the road of the same name. On a cursory inspection the bridge may appear to be cast iron but the steelwork is concealed behind a cast-iron screening arch with ornamental parapet railings and pilasters which

10   *Reinforced concrete at Stanford Bridge, 1905.*

make a bold architectural statement. The second bridge spans the River Severn just north of Bewdley in Worcestershire. It has a riveted main steel arch of 150ft with a rise of 15ft made up of four arch ribs spaced at 12ft 6in. On the west bank of the river the bridge is continued across the flood plain by five segmental blue brick arches. **Elan Valley Pipeline Bridge (WR3)** is unusual since it carries the water pipelines of the Elan Valley Aqueduct, which transports water from the Elan Valley reservoirs in Wales to Frankley Reservoir in Birmingham. An example of a steel railway bridge which has found an alternative use is the viaduct which formerly carried the Great Western Railway line between Stratford-upon-Avon and Honeybourne over the River Avon. The railway closed in the 1960s and the route is now used as a cycleway and footpath.

Only ten years after steel became a common bridge building material, a new material began to make progress – reinforced concrete. Concrete, like cast iron, is comparatively weak in tension, so the first concrete bridges were arches, using the material wholly in compression. The first bridge of this material, over the Metropolitan District Railway in west London, was fairly short-lived as it was demolished for track widening, but Homersfield Bridge of 1870 in Suffolk and Seaton Bridge of 1877 in Devon remain. To overcome the limitations on form, concrete could be reinforced by steel bars placed where tensile forces might occur. Reinforced concrete bridges were developed on the Continent by the French engineer François Hennebique and his techniques were brought to Britain under license by L.G. Mouchel. An under-strength bridge at Chewton Glen in Hampshire was strengthened by a reinforced saddle in 1900 and by 1910 bridges of the new material were becoming almost commonplace. The earliest reinforced concrete bridge in the West Midlands is situated at Stanford on Teme in Worcestershire. The arch of **Stanford Bridge (WR10)**, now by-passed by a modern concrete bridge, spans 96ft and was completed in 1905. Designed by Mouchel for J.H.Garrett, the County Surveyor, it was constructed by the Hennebique Company. The form of the bridge is reminiscent of cast-iron arches with the bridge deck supported from the arch by vertical struts. Another, similar but longer, bridge was formerly located downstream of the Iron Bridge at Coalbrookdale at Jackfield. The Free Bridge, so called as it was the only toll-free crossing of the River Severn in the area, had three spans similar to Stanford Bridge with reinforced concrete arches and vertical struts. The main span was 87ft with two side spans of 66ft. The bridge was built only four years later than Stanford, in 1909, again by the Hennebique Company and designed by Mouchel. The bridge, on an awkward alignment with a right-angled approach from the east, suffered badly from spalling concrete and vehicle damage and proved to be beyond economic repair. It was demolished in 1994 and has been replaced by a modern cable-stayed bridge of single span with a tower on the south bank (SJ 681033). This design was chosen to maintain the tradition that new bridges across the Severn Gorge should be of the most up-to-date design.

Mouchel offered his designs in competition with traditional types, making cost an important consideration, and many of the early structures had too little concrete surrounding the steel which was therefore prone to corrosion. This was the case of the Free Bridge mentioned above. Modern techniques of repair can deal with the consequences but some are uneconomic; others were simply inadequate for increased loads and so have been demolished. From the early 1900s other designers, such as the County Surveyor of Somerset, were able to provide designs that did not infringe Hennebique's patents, and reinforced concrete became almost the material of choice for new small- and medium -span bridges. The largest was the Royal Tweed Bridge of 1928 at Berwick-upon-Tweed. Within the West Midlands there are many hundreds of reinforced concrete bridges and many examples will be known to the reader. However, a new form of concrete bridge using prestressed concrete was developed during and immediately after the Second World War. Prestressed concrete seeks to overcome the tensile weakness of reinforced concrete by subjecting the structure to an initial compression by means of tensioned cables within the concrete. The tensioning can be applied prior to the pouring of the concrete into the mould ('pre-tensioning') or by wires threaded through

11 *The Free Bridge with loading relieved by a Bailey bridge.*

12 *The New Free Bridge.*

ducts in the hardened concrete after it is cast ('post-tensioning'). Thus, when tensile forces are applied to the concrete, these forces, instead of inducing tensile stresses, tend to reduce the prestressed compression and thus avoid the cracking of the concrete which might otherwise occur. In addition to reducing the likelihood of tensile cracking, prestressing also usually results in a more slender structure since the concrete is being used more efficiently.

As with reinforced concrete, the first prestressed concrete bridges in Britain were based on Continental practice. The initial impetus came in 1940 when it was expected that significant numbers of bridges might be destroyed by enemy action, and a stock of precast, prestressed beams was made for emergency use. In fact only two such bridges were constructed. In 1946 similar beams were used in rebuilding Adam Viaduct, Wigan, the first prestressed railway underbridge in the country. Two years later the first post-tensioned bridge was completed at Fishtoft near Boston; it has a 72ft clear span. What was claimed the following year to be the first prestressed portal frame in the world was a footbridge in The Parks at Oxford, and a span of 160ft at a Rotherham steelworks in 1952 was thought to be the longest railway underbridge in the world.

The first major prestressed concrete road bridge in Britain, in 1954 at Southampton, was not pleasing aesthetically, but from 1958 onwards, starting at Clifton Bridge in Nottingham, the comparative lightness of prestressed compared with reinforced concrete enabled designers to provide many elegant structures. Prestressing, combined with modern design tools, has also made possible new techniques of construction. Balanced cantilever methods were used to good effect at Medway Bridge in 1964 with a main span of 500ft. The longest span in prestressed concrete is 190 metres at Orwell Bridge but it is outranked by the 233 metres of the Foyle Bridge, below Derry, in steel.

One of the most common uses of prestressed concrete beams has been in motorway construction where a number of standard bridge designs have been developed for use in specific locations. Probably the most extensive use of such beams is on the Midland Links motorway project, where elevated sections of the M6 and M5 run through Birmingham and the Black Country. The viaducts are formed from prestressed concrete beams supported by concrete trestles. **Gravelly Hill Interchange (WM6)**, at the time of its construction in 1968 the most complex motorway junction in Britain, is a prime example of this type of construction.

For longer spans cable-stayed or suspension bridges are the rule and for 20 years from 1981 the world's longest span was the Humber Bridge. However, the West Midlands, with the exception of the Severn Valley, does not contain any large rivers; consequently the use of long span bridges is relatively rare. However, there are examples and some of the more interesting ones are quoted below.

Early suspension bridges used iron chains to support the bridge deck since steel wire was not available in sufficient quantities. The classic example is Thomas Telford's great suspension bridge which carried his improved Holyhead Road over the Menai Straits to Anglesey with a span of 579ft. The West Midlands cannot boast a span as great as this but a fine example is to be found carrying a footway across the site of the former goods yard at **Whitchurch Station (SH35)** in Shropshire. This bridge, which dates from about 1874, has a main span of 120ft and the footway is suspended from two wrought-iron chains made up from flat wrought-iron bars. The towers of the bridge are, unusually, in timber.

Stapenhill Bridge (ST4), at Burton upon Trent, is a footbridge over the River Trent with its unusual suspension chains formed from horizontal flat plates riveted together to give a suspension chain eight inches by 1½ inches. The joints between adjacent plates in the chain are staggered to give one joint every six feet. The main span of the

13 *The Menai Bridge, designed by Thomas Telford, 1826.*

bridge is 120ft. On the north side of the bridge the footway is carried over low-lying ground adjacent to the river by a raised causeway over 1,600ft long. The causeway, with 81 spans, is supported by cast-iron columns. The bridge and causeway complex also includes two small covered areas about 15ft long which may have been provided to give shelter to persons using the causeway in inclement weather as its location is very exposed. It was opened in April 1889 and built by a local firm, Thornewill & Wareham. Another suspension footbridge, this time across the River Wye in Hereford, is **Victoria Bridge (HE4)**.

In Leamington Spa can be found a suspension bridge whose form is a distant precursor of modern-cable stayed bridges. **Mill Road Bridge (WK21)** carries a footway over the River Leam in Jepson Gardens and was designed by the then borough engineer of Leamington Spa, William de Normanville. Opened in 1903, the bridge has a span of 100ft. Instead of the traditional supporting cables or chains, the bridge deck is supported at the third points of its span by circular suspension rods. At each end and each side of the bridge two rods run from the top of the 19ft-high towers to the nearer third point and one rod runs to the farther third point. Thus each third point is supported by three rods, two from the nearer tower and one from the farther tower.

Porthill Bridge (SH29), a more conventional suspension bridge with wire rope suspension cables, crosses the River Severn in Shrewsbury to link Quarry Park with the district of Porthill. This bridge, which has a span of 180ft, was opened on 18 January 1923 and carries a footway across the river. The designers were David Rowell & Co. of Westminster using one of their standard designs.

From time to time, bridges are constructed with very limited headroom underneath. This is usually due to the configuration of the land which precludes the raised approach a more conventional bridge would require. In such cases where it is necessary to provide increased headroom for traffic passing under the bridge, a moveable span may be provided. There are many examples of such bridges on the canal network of the West Midlands and these are of two main types. On the Oxford Canal may be found the simplest type consisting of a single timber span across the canal which is pivoted at one end. A counterbalance weight in the form of two extended arms is provided and the bridge may be lifted to an angle by pulling down on the counterbalance arms. Although the bridge is not in the vertical position when raised, sufficient room is provided for a boat to pass through the gap. A more complex form of the bridge, reminiscent of many such bridges in the Netherlands, exists on several canals in the area, notably the Ellesmere Canal Llangollen Branch (now more usually called the Llangollen Canal) and the Stratford-upon-Avon Canal. This type of bridge has a single (or in some rare cases

14 *Lifting bridge, Oxford Canal.*

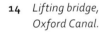

a double) lifting span which is raised by an overhead mechanism with a counterweight on the end of the upper section. A few of these bridges have been mechanised but normally they are raised by pulling or winching down the upper section, thus raising the far end of the span.

An alternative method of raising the bridge is by lifting the whole span vertically from both ends. An example of this type is **Tipton Lift Bridge (WM20)** which was originally sited at the Five Ways basin of the Birmingham Canal but was moved to an arm of the canal at the Black Country Museum for preservation. The bridge is lifted by four chains which pass over large chain wheels fixed at the tops of vertical columns. At each end of the bridge the two supporting chains are connected to a common counterbalance weight running across the width of the bridge. The bridge is raised by a hand winch. The bridge was built in 1922 by the Great Western Railway, the builders being Armstrong Whitworth of Newcastle upon Tyne.

One type of bridge, of which numerous examples are found all over the region, is the canal aqueduct. Normally the aqueduct will carry the waterway over a stream or river or, less often, over a road, but three examples will be quoted later of a rarer type where the waterway is carried over another canal.

Canal aqueducts mainly date from the mid- to late 18th century during the heyday of canal building (see Chapter 2). Early examples are of the 'Brindley' type where the entire canal, including its puddled clay bed, is carried over the structure. The massive weight to be carried required the provision of a structure with small span masonry arches and thick piers. Examples of this type can be found on many of the early canals. On the Staffordshire & Worcestershire Canal, near its junction with the Trent & Mersey Canal at Great Haywood in Staffordshire, there are two examples. The most northerly, the **Trent Aqueduct (ST16)**, carries the canal over the river and has four small segmental arches of about 21ft span. Its engineer was the pioneer James Brindley and the aqueduct was built on dry land in a loop of the river, which was then diverted to run under it.

Only a short distance south of the River Trent the canal also crosses the River Sow on **Milford Aqueduct (ST21)**, a similar structure, with four spans of 22ft. The massive piers are 3ft 3in wide. Both these aqueducts were built around 1771-2.

In 1795 Thomas Telford was appointed Engineer for the Shrewsbury Canal, succeeding Josiah Clowes who had recently died. Where the canal crosses the River Tern, Telford designed **Longdon upon Tern Aqueduct (SH17)**, a cast-iron aqueduct which opened in 1796 and was the first major cast-iron canal aqueduct to be built. The waterway was carried in a cast-iron trough nine feet wide and three feet deep made up from cast-iron plates bolted together with the towpath alongside the south side of the trough, level with its base. The slender lines of the trough and its three-legged vertical and inclined cruciform cast-iron supports are in contrast with the heavy masonry abutments and traditional small 'Brindley' arches at each end.

With the experience gained at Longdon upon Tern, Telford, who was also General Agent and Engineer for the Ellesmere Canal, then under construction through Shropshire and the Welsh Border, together with the Chief Engineer William Jessop, designed two high-level aqueducts on the Ellesmere Canal. The first, **Chirk Aqueduct (SH10)** across the valley of the River Ceriog, has masonry piers, but the canal was contained in a trough with waterproofed masonry sides and a cast-iron plate base. The cast-iron side plates, visible today, were a later addition. The total length of the aqueduct, with its 10 40ft span arches is 710ft and the waterway is carried 70ft above the river. It was opened in 1801. Four miles further west Telford and Jessop built the great Pontcysyllte Aqueduct which carries the canal over the Vale of Llangollen. The foundation stone was laid in July 1795 and the aqueduct was opened in November 1805. At 120ft above

15 *Ellesmere Canal, Chirk Aqueduct.*

the River Dee and 1,007ft long, it is the longest in Britain but that structure is outside the scope of this volume. However, the West Midlands is the location for the second longest cast-iron aqueduct in Britain. **Bearley (or Edstone) Aqueduct (WK1)** on the Stratford-upon-Avon Canal north of Stratford has a cast-iron trough just under 500ft long supported on 14 brick piers. The towpath of the canal is carried on an extension of the base plates of the trough. The Engineer for this section of the canal was William Whitmore, a manufacturer and ironfounder in Birmingham, who was appointed in January 1811 although he had little experience of such work. His work on the aqueducts is regarded as somewhat old-fashioned.

In the West Midlands region are three examples of a relatively rare type of aqueduct – one which carries the line of one canal over another. Two of these are situated in the Birmingham area and date from the time of Thomas Telford's improvements to the main line of the Birmingham Canal in 1828-9 (see Chapter 2 for more details). Telford's main work involved the cutting of a new, lower-level line through the hill at Smethwick. At the west end of the cutting the old main line crosses the new line, 20ft lower. **Steward Aqueduct (WM27)** has two brick skew semi-elliptical arches with spans of 28ft 3in. The upper waterway is carried in a clay-puddle-lined trough which accounts for the relatively massive form of the aqueduct. Telford's resident engineer for the construction of this aqueduct (and for most of the work carried out under Telford's improvements) was William Mackenzie, who went on to become a major contractor in railway construction. Towards the east end of Smethwick cutting a branch canal leading to the site of the Smethwick Engine, which pumped water to the canal system, also crosses Telford's new line. For this location Telford designed **Engine Arm Aqueduct (WM22)**, an elegant cast-iron aqueduct with a segmental arch spanning 52ft. In this case the waterway is contained within a cast-iron trough, the reduced weight leading to a lighter structure.

The form of the arch is reminiscent of the early cast-iron bridges designed by Telford in Shropshire, mentioned above.

At Hazlehurst in Staffordshire the Caldon Canal branches at its eastern end into two waterways. Its main line leads eastward towards Froghall and Uttoxeter while the other branch leads northwards to Leek. The junction between the two canals has been altered several times and in its present form, dating from 1841, the Leek branch runs to the south of the main line before crossing it on **Hazlehurst Aqueduct (ST8)**. The aqueduct has a single semi-circular brick arch spanning about 27ft, the difference in level of the two canals being about 26ft.

It can be seen from this chapter that bridge construction has been a major feature of the work of the civil engineer since time immemorial. The design and construction of bridges has responded to changes in form and materials, from arch bridges in timber, stone and brick, through cast-iron arches and wrought-iron trusses, to steel and reinforced and prestressed concrete arches and beams. Generally, bridges continue to serve the need for which they were initially built and many older bridges have survived, albeit with widening and other modifications to make them more amenable to modern traffic conditions.

Until the middle of the 18th century life for the majority of Britons had not changed greatly since the Middle Ages, but in the next 200 years the pace of change accelerated rapidly. For any significant industrial development to take place there must exist four components. Three of these are: firstly a source of raw materials; secondly, an industrial process to manufacture the finished product; and thirdly, a market into which the finished product may be sold. The fourth component, linking the other three, is transport. As an example, consider the manufacture of bricks. This requires the existence of a source of suitable clay as a raw material and the existence of a brick-making plant with kilns to produce the finished product. The bricks are then sold to local building projects.

For a village-based economy the transport needs are relatively small scale. In the brick-making example the clay pit will be near at hand, the manufactory situated in or near the village and the bricks sold in the locality. However, for large-scale industrialisation to develop with manufacturing in large units (factories), the whole scale of the operation needs to be increased and this will require a much more sophisticated transport system capable of providing long-range, large payload, capacity at a reasonable cost. Thus for industrialisation to take place it was necessary to develop improved transport systems.

In the early days of industrialisation only two modes of suitable transport were available; road-based and river-based. Carriage of goods by road in the 18th century was a slow, dangerous and expensive undertaking. Many roads, especially in rural areas, were passable only with difficulty in the winter months and even in summer, due to a lack of any scientific approach to road construction and maintenance, and the general condition of the roads was very poor. The way in which roads developed will be considered in detail in Chapter 4. This chapter will consider the development of the other main mode of transport, inland waterways.

The use of rivers for navigation in Britain dates from the earliest times. After the end of the Roman occupation, roads generally fell into a state of disrepair and rivers provided an alternative means of transport for freight and passengers. The major rivers, notably the Thames, Severn, Trent, Mersey and Irwell, were important arteries of trade and it is no surprise to find that early industrial developments often took place along their banks. The development in the West Midlands of the iron-founding industry at Coalbrookdale (later Ironbridge) on the banks of the River Severn is a typical example since at that location there was situated a source of raw materials for the production of the iron and the river provided the convenient transport system vital for industrial-scale development to take place.

Rivers were also a convenient source of power, as discussed in Chapter 5, and early attempts to improve the navigation of rivers often gave rise to conflicts between the navigators and the mill owners, who regarded navigation as a threat to their water supplies. However, rivers were successfully improved by the provision of weirs which increased river levels, with flash or pound locks to allow boats to pass the weirs and in some cases by constructing lengths of artificial waterway to by-pass difficult lengths of river. Flash locks were simply single gates set in the weir which could be opened to allow boats to run downstream with the resultant 'flash' of water or to be hauled laboriously upstream against the stream of water flowing through the opening in the weir. Closing the gate after the passage of a boat allowed the water level upstream of the weir to regain its original level. A pound lock, with two sets of gates, developed by the Chinese long ago, overcomes the problem of significant loss of water from upstream

by restricting the loss to the capacity of the lock chamber. The technology will be familiar: the boat enters the lock chamber, the gates are closed and the chamber is filled or emptied as appropriate. When the levels have equalised, the gates are opened and the boat leaves the lock at the new level.

17 *River Exe basin at Exeter.*

One early example of river improvement is the improvement of the River Exe under an Act of 1539 whereby a length of canal parallel with the river was constructed, and later extended, which eventually allowed craft of 150 tons to reach the basin in Exeter.

Geographically, the West Midlands is largely devoid of major navigable rivers, being situated largely on a high plateau straddling the national watershed. The exception is the River Severn and its tributaries situated on the western flank of the area. The River Severn was a major artery of river trade, having been navigable as far upstream as Pool Quay, near Welshpool. There were numerous Acts of Parliament dating from as early as 1503 concerning the navigation of the river, with several concerned with the establishment of a towing path for horses that eventually extended from Gloucester to Shrewsbury. Inland ports developed along the river, the most important being Gloucester, Worcester, Tewkesbury, Bewdley and Bridgnorth. Tributaries of the Severn were also important navigations including the Warwickshire Avon, which had been made navigable from its junction with the Severn at Tewkesbury to Stratford-upon-Avon by William Sandys about 1639 using 13 flash and pound locks. Acts controlling the navigation on the river were passed in 1751 and 1793. The River Stour in Worcestershire was improved for navigation by Andrew Yarranton who was prominent in the development of river navigation both in the West Midlands and elsewhere. Between 1665 and 1667 he improved the river with locks but the river fell into disrepair by the end of the 18th century. Other tributaries of the Severn which have been used for navigation at some time include the Dick Brook, near Worcester, another project of Andrew Yarranton, the River Teme (although doubt has been expressed that this river was navigable above Powick) and the River Salwarpe. As will be seen later, many canals made junctions with the River Severn which continued to be a major artery of trade in the area until modern times.

Purely artificial waterways (canals) in Britain date from Roman times with the building of the Fossdyke from Torksey on the River Trent to Lincoln, a distance of 11 miles, improved during the reign of King Henry I in 1121. One of the earliest canals in Britain was the 6½-mile Stamford Canal, part of the Welland Navigation, which was authorised by an Act of 1571 although not completed until about 1670. However, the large-scale building of canals dates from the mid-18th century, starting with the cutting of the 18½-mile Newry Canal in Northern Ireland in 1742 (the first summit-level canal) quickly followed in the north of England by the Sankey Brook navigation in 1757 and the Bridgewater Canal in 1761. Initially running between the Duke of Bridgewater's collieries at Worsley into Manchester, the Bridgewater Canal was later extended along the south side of the River Mersey to a junction with the river at Runcorn, thus bypassing the Mersey and Irwell Navigation.

Due to the success of these early canals and the region's lack of navigable rivers, the West Midlands became a natural target for many of the next series of canals to be promoted, supported by the Duke of Bridgewater's agent John Gilbert and the Staffordshire potter Josiah Wedgwood. James Brindley (see below), who had been the Duke's Engineer, was instrumental as engineer in all these early schemes until his death in 1772.

The first four canals to be promoted in the Midlands enabled the linking of the four major navigable rivers, the Trent, Mersey, Severn and Thames, by canals crossing the region, with a branch from the west into the heart of the developing industrial region around Birmingham.

The longest of the four was the Trent & Mersey Canal. It was 93½ miles long and commenced at a junction with the Bridgewater Canal at Preston Brook. From Preston Brook it ran south, climbing to reach a summit level just north of the ridge at Harecastle, which it passed though by way of **Harecastle Tunnel (ST27)**. This tunnel, 2,880 yards long, was in itself a major undertaking and its narrow bore took nine years to complete. South of Harecastle Tunnel the canal entered the valley of the River Trent, which it followed closely through Stoke-on-Trent and Great Haywood. Curving east then north-east the canal passed through Lichfield and Burton upon Trent before making a junction with the River Trent at Wilden Ferry. At its northern end between Preston Brook and Middlewich and at its southern end between Burton upon Trent and Wilden Ferry the canal was wide enough for boats 14ft wide, the remaining central section being the narrow seven-foot-wide gauge. This canal was particularly important to the Wedgwood potteries since it provided a convenient transport route to Burslem for China clay from the West Country via Liverpool and the Mersey and flint from East Anglia via the River Trent, and the export of finished china products from Burslem to markets in London and elsewhere. Indeed, the line of the canal passed immediately by the entrance to Wedgwood's works and boats could be loaded and unloaded directly into the works. Cutting of the canal started in July 1766 and it was finally completed in May 1777 following the completion of Harecastle Tunnel.

It should be mentioned here that the building of the early canals was usually a lengthy process, often due to shortage of finances, and it was the custom when a length of canal had been finished to fill the canal with water and use it for construction traffic or local trade until the whole route was completed. This arrangement also had the benefit of providing some income for the canal company, often at a time when funds were running low.

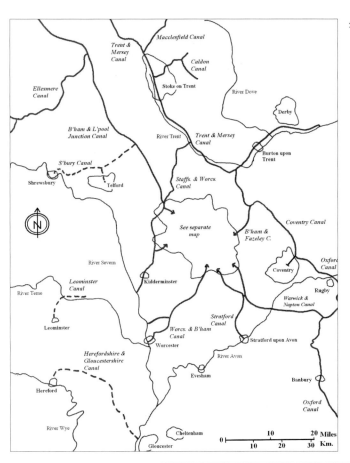

18 *Map of regional canals and rivers.*

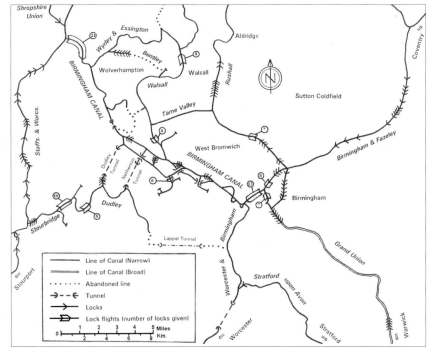

19 *Map of canals in Birmingham.*

20 *Stourport – Clock Warehouse.*

It is a common misapprehension that canals are stagnant ditches; in fact they carry a significant flow of water from the summit level downwards. Each time a boat passes through a lock a large amount of water passes from the higher to the lower level. To ensure that the canal remains navigable it is necessary to replace this water at the summit level of the canal. Therefore the canal engineer diverted as much water as possible into the higher reaches of the waterway. Direct abstraction from rivers and streams might be possible but was often restricted owing to the demands of other water users, notably mill owners. To compensate for periods of low rainfall when water supplies would be restricted it was usual to provide reservoirs. The capacity of a reservoir would often be given in terms of the numbers of locks full of water it held. The problem of ensuring adequate water supplies led to experiments being carried out with various types of inclined planes or vertical lifts, but these were largely unsuccessful although a number of inclined planes operated on a local canal network in east Shropshire.

The other three canals were promoted to complete the network linking the four major rivers of England and thus provided a more reliable freight transport system for the nation. These canals were the Staffordshire & Worcestershire, the Coventry and the Oxford canals.

The Staffordshire & Worcestershire was the first canal of the quartet to be completed. Its 46-mile length started from a junction with the Trent & Mersey Canal at Great Haywood. From here it ran southwards, climbing to a summit level at Gailey then following the valley of the Smestow Brook and the River Stour to join the River Severn at Stourport on Severn. There were two short tunnels and several aqueducts on the canal, and Compton Lock was the first lock constructed by James Brindley. There were two sets of staircase locks, at Botterham with two locks and at Bratch, near Wombourne in Staffordshire, where the canal descended 30ft 2in by means of three locks. At a later date the locks at Bratch were converted into three closely spaced separate locks with long side ponds which even today require careful operation to avoid flooding the surrounding area. Stourport was a 'new town' created to serve the basins and locks connecting the canal to the river and enabling cargoes to be transhipped between the canal boats and the Severn barges. The area around the basins still retains some of the atmosphere of the original canal town, with the *Tontine Inn*, built about the same time as the basins, and the **Clock Warehouse (WR11)** of *c.*1800 being particularly noteworthy. From Stourport barges could navigate the River Severn upstream to Pool Quay and downstream to Gloucester. Building of the canal started in 1766 and it was finally opened throughout on 25 May 1772. The Clerk of Works, who would supervise the construction works in Brindley's absence, was John Baker with John Fennyhouse Green as his Under Clerk. Thomas Dadford senior had been appointed as a carpenter and joiner to the canal company in 1767 and was responsible for the construction of the River Sow aqueduct and reportedly the basins and river locks at Stourport. Following the opening of the canal he was appointed Engineer to the company. In later years he was involved in the construction of many canals including the Stourbridge and Dudley Canals, the Cromford Canal in Derbyshire and the Glamorganshire and Montgomeryshire Canals in Wales. As would be normal for the construction of the early canals, contracts were for relatively short lengths of canal cutting, individual bridges or other structures. One of the most prominent contractors was John Beswick; others included William Bowker, William Wright, Jonathan Gee and James Hogg.

Two other canals provided the link between the Trent & Mersey Canal and the River Thames at Oxford and thus would complete Brindley's 'grand cross' of canals linking all the major rivers of central England. The 38-mile Coventry Canal commenced at a basin just to the north of Coventry city centre and ran north via Atherstone and Tamworth to make a junction with the Trent & Mersey Canal at Fradley near Lichfield. Started in April 1768, it was not finally completed until July 1790. The company suffered severe financial difficulties and cutting of the canal ceased when it had reached Atherstone from Coventry in 1771. Under the Coleshill Agreement of 1782 between the Birmingham & Fazeley, Trent & Mersey, Coventry and Oxford Canals the work was completed by other companies. The section between Fradley and Whittington Brook was built by the Trent & Mersey and between Whittington Brook and Fazeley junction by the Birmingham & Fazeley Canal Company. This latter section remained the property of the Fazeley company.

21   *Oxford Canal near Wormleighton.*

The Oxford Canal commenced at a junction at Hawkesbury with the Coventry Canal and ran south 91 miles by way of Rugby and Banbury; then, following the valley of the River Cherwell, it joined the River Thames just north of Oxford. Started in 1769 this canal was also delayed by shortage of finance. It reached Banbury from the north in March 1778 but made no further progress until the Coleshill Agreement (referred to above), following which it was completed to Oxford between 1786 and 1790. The alignment of the canal was particularly sinuous, following the contours closely presumably to avoid the expense of cuttings and embankments although there was a shallow tunnel 1,138 yards long at **Fenny Compton (WK10)**. The Coventry and the Oxford canal companies could not agree upon a location for the junction between the two canals and between 1777 and 1785 the two canals ran parallel for over one mile to a junction at Longford. In 1785 the junction was relocated to its present site at Hawkesbury. Later, between 1829 and 1832, the line of the northern section of the canal was shortened between Hawkesbury and Braunston by cutting through some of the old loops. Where the old loop was still required for navigation a series of cast-iron arch towpath bridges was provided to carry the towpath of the new line across the old loop. This shortened the total distance between Hawkesbury and Oxford from 91 miles to 75 miles. Later the tunnel at Fenny Compton was opened out to form a deep cutting, the work being completed in two stages between 1865 and 1870. During the opening out of the tunnel a brickworks was established alongside the tunnel and large

22   *Brick kiln at site of Fenny Compton tunnel.*

23 *Narrow boat at Ellesmere Port Boat Museum.*

quantities of bricks were made from the excavated clay. The remains of the kiln are still visible at the top of the cutting today. In 1837 a fine new cast-iron footbridge was erected to carry the towpath of the Coventry Canal over the junction at **Hawkesbury (WK6)**. Even today the U-turn required to proceed from the Coventry onto the Oxford Canal presents difficulties for boats.

These four Brindley canals were 'narrow' canals. That is, they were designed for boats about 70ft long and seven feet beam, the traditional 'narrow boat'. These dimensions fixed the size of the locks on the canal and therefore prevented the use of longer or wider craft. There were, of course, no mechanical aids to canal cutting and all work was by manual labour. Generally contracts were let for short lengths of canal and the men engaged on this work became known as 'navigators', or 'navvies' for short, an appellation which persisted into the railway building era for men engaged in civil engineering construction work.

James Brindley, born in Derbyshire in 1716, was trained as a millwright and built many wind and water mills, demonstrating his talent for theory and practice in mechanics and hydraulics. By 1758 he had begun his association with canals, having surveyed a route for a canal from Stoke-on-Trent to Wilden Ferry on the River Trent. In 1759 he began his collaboration with the Duke of Bridgewater, surveying the line of the Bridgewater Canal. He rapidly became a leading figure in canal design and construction and was engaged by most of the early canal promoters as their Engineer. Canals in the West Midlands with which he was closely associated were the Trent & Mersey, the Staffordshire & Worcestershire, the Droitwich, the Coventry, the Birmingham and the Oxford. James Brindley died in September 1772, still working on a canal survey.

The final work in this early set of canals was the Birmingham Canal, which ran for 22½ miles from Aldersley junction on the Staffordshire & Worcestershire Canal near Wolverhampton to a series of basins and wharves in central Birmingham. Four years in construction, the canal opened in September 1772. There was a short branch to Wednesbury which opened earlier to gain access to important coal mines there. Along its route the canal passed over high ground at Smethwick, resulting in a very short summit pound and causing difficulties with water supply. By 1790 the summit level had been lowered by 18ft, eliminating three locks on either side of the summit. As described below, Thomas Telford later carried out extensive improvement works on the canal. Most of the canal basins in central Birmingham have over the intervening years been filled in and built over but **Gas Street Basin (WM5)** remains today and, suitably refurbished, forms a reminder of the earlier age.

An important link in the West Midlands canal system was the Birmingham & Fazeley Canal, which opened in August 1789. This canal ran north-eastwards from Old Turn junction in the centre of the city to a junction with the Coventry Canal at Fazeley. It provided a link from Birmingham to the north east via the Coventry and Trent & Mersey Canals. In its length of 15 miles the canal had 38 locks, and a major feature, which was to prove troublesome later, was the flight of 13 locks at **Farmers Bridge (WM4)** at the start of the canal in Birmingham, with a total fall of about 90ft over a distance of a thousand yards. This was intensively used as it formed the only link between the western and eastern sections of the Birmingham canal system until the opening of the Tame Valley Canal in 1844. In 1803 six men were employed to assist boats through the locks and in 1818 gas lighting was installed to permit night working. It is recorded that in March 1841 4,877 boats passed through the top lock.

A feature of the landscape of the Black Country is the prominent limestone ridge which runs north-west to south-east through Dudley. This ridge formed a barrier to canal communication but an early development in the area on the west side of the ridge was the Stourbridge Canal, opened in December 1779. It ran from the Staffordshire & Worcestershire Canal at Stourton junction to Black Delph, with a branch to Stourbridge and a later extension, the Stourbridge Extension Canal, a further two miles northwards, opened in June 1840. Also in 1779 the first line of the Dudley Canal opened. It ran for 4½ miles between the Stourbridge Canal at Black Delph and Parkhead. Lord Dudley and Ward had opened limestone quarries at Castle Hill on the north side of the ridge and constructed a short branch canal from the Birmingham Canal to the quarries. This canal passed through a short tunnel into the limestone workings. In July 1785 an Act was obtained to link this canal to the Dudley Canal by driving a tunnel under the limestone ridge. Work on driving the 3,172-yard **Dudley Tunnel (WM18)** and the approach canal on the south side from Parkhead commenced in October 1785, the line of the tunnel being set out by John Snape and Abraham Lees under the supervision of the Company's consultant, Thomas Dadford senior. The contractor was John Pinkerton but after problems in 1787 the work was transferred to a direct labour force. From 1789 the Engineer for the tunnel construction was Josiah Clowes. After delays the tunnel was finally opened in June 1792, thus connecting the Dudley canal to the main Birmingham system. In 1798 the Dudley Canal was later extended by its No. 2 line 11 miles eastward from Parkhead through the 3,795-yard-long Lappal Tunnel to join the Worcester & Birmingham Canal at Selly Oak junction, providing a further link between the western and eastern canals. Dudley Tunnel remained the only north-to-south connection under the Dudley ridge until the opening in 1858 of **Netherton Tunnel (WM19)** linking the Dudley Canal No. 2 line to the Birmingham Canal. This, the last great canal tunnel to be built in Britain, was brick-lined throughout and of large dimensions, with a waterway 17ft wide and two towpaths.

Josiah Clowes was born in 1735 in north Staffordshire and was involved in many early canal projects both as a contractor and engineer. In addition to the Dudley Tunnel he worked on the Trent & Mersey, Stroudwater, Herefordshire & Gloucestershire and Worcester & Birmingham Canals. He was at work on the Shrewsbury Canal when he died in December 1794, being succeeded on that project by Thomas Telford. John Pinkerton was the most prominent member of an extensive family associated as contractors with early canal building. His father, James Pinkerton, had worked on drainage work in the East Riding of Yorkshire and John, having started working with his father in 1770, commenced working on his own account from about 1780. He was involved with many canal schemes but although much of his work was satisfactory he also encountered difficulties with the quality of his work on several contracts. In 1787 he was released from his contact on Dudley Tunnel after complaints about lack of progress, poor quality bricks in the tunnel lining and rising costs.

The commercial success of these early canal companies sparked off a massive increase in canal promotion, the period from about 1790 to 1797 seeing the authorisation of 53 new canals and many more schemes that never reached the stage of Parliamentary sanction. This period is often referred to as the 'Canal Mania'. Inevitably, many of the canals which were built during this period were not commercially successful, quite a few of the unsuccessful canals being built in agricultural areas with local finance for local purposes. However, many miles of canal were built and satisfied the increasing demand for freight transport, a consequence of the large-scale industrialisation taking place in the latter half of the 18th century.

The Worcester & Birmingham Canal had been opened in December 1815 and ran from **Gas Street Basin (WM5)**, where it met the Birmingham Canal, to the River Severn at Diglis Basin, Worcester. The canal thus provided an alternative, more direct, route to the Staffordshire & Worcestershire Canal. A major feature of this canal, apart from five tunnels including the 2,726-yard Wast Hill tunnel, was the great flight of locks at **Tardebigge (WR13)**. With 30 locks, Tardebigge is the greatest lock flight in Britain. It carries the canal down 217ft over a length of about 2¼ miles, from the Birmingham plateau into the valley of the River Severn. The top lock at Tardebigge is especially notable as it has a large rise of 12ft, roughly twice the normal rise of a narrow lock. This was the result of the lock having been the site of an experimental vertical lift, designed by John Woodhouse and installed in 1808. The lift consisted of a tank suspended by chains passing over large wheels and counterbalanced by brick weights. Trials of the lift were held between 1808 and 1813 but by January 1811 the Company had decided to use conventional locks instead of lifts and the lift had been replaced by the present top lock by 1815. At **Gas Street Basin (WM5)** the Birmingham Canal refused to allow a physical junction between the two canals and for 20 years the two canals were separated by the 'Worcester Bar', a narrow strip of land about seven feet wide, across which all goods passing between the two canals had to be transhipped. In 1815, however, a lock was installed through the Bar, the site of which can still be seen today although the canals are now at the same level and the lock gates have been removed.

24 *Canal offices and Worcester Bar at Gas Street by the Worcester & Birmingham Canal.*

One further canal linking the Birmingham area to the south was the Stratford-upon-Avon Canal. This canal commenced at a junction with the Worcester & Birmingham Canal at Kings Norton and ran south-east and south to make a junction with the River Avon at Stratford-upon-Avon. Construction started from the Kings Norton end in November 1793 with Josiah Clowes as Engineer. The canal was opened as far as Hockley Heath in May 1796 but the money was then exhausted and cutting ceased. Construction restarted in 1800, this time with Samuel

25   *Saltisford Basin, Warwick, on the Warwick & Birmingham Canal.*

Porter as Engineer (Josiah Clowes having died in 1794) and reached Kingswood where, again, cutting ceased. At Kingswood there was a connection to the Warwick & Birmingham Canal which had recently opened. Finally the section southwards to Stratford-upon-Avon was commenced in 1812 with William Whitmore as Engineer and it finally reached the River Avon in June 1816. The canal is notable for a series of lifting bridges and also for three cast-iron aqueducts. The aqueducts at **Wootton Wawen (WK45)** and **Bearley (or Edstone) (WK1)** are original but the short aqueduct at **Yarningale (WK46)** was built to replace an earlier structure destroyed by a flood caused by a burst on the nearby Warwick & Birmingham Canal in 1834. Edstone aqueduct has the distinction of being the second longest cast-iron aqueduct in Britain with the total length of its 14 spans being just under 500ft. At Stratford-upon-Avon the canal made a junction with the horse-drawn Stratford & Moreton Tramway which, opened in 1826, was one of Britain's earliest railways, described in Chapter 3.

Two important later canals were the Warwick & Birmingham and the Warwick & Napton canals. The Warwick & Birmingham, opened in 1799, ran from a junction with the Birmingham canal system at Digbeth to Saltisford Basin in Warwick. At Warwick it made a junction with the Warwick & Napton Canal which continued the line to Napton junction where it joined the Oxford Canal. The Warwick & Napton also opened in 1799. A notable feature of the Warwick & Birmingham Canal is the great flight of 21 locks at **Hatton (WK16)** which carry the canal 146ft 6in down into the valley of the River Avon at Warwick, which is crossed by a stone aqueduct. These two canals later became part of the Grand Union Canal and from 1932 to 1934 the canals were widened and the locks rebuilt to permit wide boats of 14ft beam to pass along the canal, both canals having been originally

built for narrow boats only seven feet wide. Although the use of the wider boats was not great, the wider locks enabled a pair of narrow boats to enter the lock chamber side by side, reducing the time taken to pass through each lock.

In the west of the region there were several canal developments. A canal was built by Brindley – his only one open when he died – to Droitwich from the River Severn, which opened in 1771 primarily to tap the trade in salt from that town. This canal replaced the abortive attempt to make the River Salwarpe navigable. The canal was extended in 1853 by way of the Droitwich Junction Canal to join the Worcester & Birmingham Canal at Hanbury Wharf and thus open up a route to the east.

Less successful were two canal projects further west. The Leominster Canal was promoted to link Herefordshire with the River Severn and the proposed line was surveyed by Thomas Dadford junior. The canal was to be 46 miles long from Stourport on the Severn to Kington via Leominster. There were to be three tunnels of which the longest, Pensax Tunnel at 3,860 yards, would have been the longest in Britain at that time. Unfortunately the canal was never completed as planned but a section from Leominster 18½ miles to Southnet was opened in 1796 and was used for local transport. Although efforts were made to extend the canal further, Pensax tunnel was started but not completed and Southnet Tunnel collapsed during construction and was not repaired. In 1847 an Act was obtained to enable the canal to be sold to the Shrewsbury & Hereford Railway but the sale was not completed until 1858. The canal was drained in 1859 and some of the route east of Woofferton was sold to the Tenbury Railway which used the canal bed for part of its track bed.

The Herefordshire & Gloucestershire Canal was another attempt to provide a transport facility west of the River Severn. The proposed route of the canal was from the River Severn at Over, just north-west of Gloucester, 34 miles to Hereford. Construction began on the section from Over to Ledbury and this length was opened in March 1798. The Engineer was Josiah Clowes until his death, when Robert Whitworth senior took over. Beyond Ledbury no further work was done until the project was revived in 1839 with Stephen Ballard as Engineer and the canal was completed to Hereford in May 1845. There were three tunnels including Oxenhall with a length of 2,192 yards. At **Monkhide (HE9)**, east of Hereford, Ballard built a bridge with an extremely skewed span to carry a minor road across the canal, a somewhat unusual arrangement given that on such a minor road the road would often have been diverted to cross the canal at right angles.

While all these developments had been taking place, the expansion of the Birmingham canal system had been proceeding rapidly. The development of the Birmingham Canal Navigations to the north of Birmingham included the Wyrley & Essington (1792), the Walsall (1799), the Bentley (1843) and the Rushall (1847) Canals which were reaching north into the Cannock coalfields. A significant development was the provision of the 8½-mile Tame Valley Canal which linked the western side of the network to the Birmingham & Fazeley Canal. It opened in 1844, well into the railway era to which its bold engineering, with deep cuttings and high embankments, bears a resemblance, and provided a much needed by-pass for the Farmers Bridge lock flight, then heavily congested. Eventually the Birmingham canal network extended to over 200 miles of canal with a complex water management system linking the various levels.

One network dating from the early days of canals remained isolated from the national system until 1835, and was to be found in east Shropshire. Between what is now Telford and Shrewsbury was a network of canals of relatively short length but which incorporated some important early developments in canal technology. The canals were built to serve the new industrial developments which sprang up in the area in the late 18th century and the earliest, opened in July 1768, was the Donnington Wood Canal. This was a tub-boat canal 5½ miles long built by Earl Gower & Company and included a vertical lift, later converted to an inclined plane, as an alternative to conventional locks. It was linked to navigable levels at Donnington Wood mines. The boats which used the canal were only 19ft 8in long and carried about three tons. The whole canal including a two-mile branch was disused by 1904. The next canals to be opened were the Wombridge Canals and the Ketley Canal, opened about 1788. These were also tub-boat canals of less than two miles in length but the Ketley Canal had an inclined plane at Ketley which is said to have been the earliest to be built on a canal in Britain. Of greater extent was the Shropshire Canal, opened in 1792. This canal, which ran from the Donnington Wood Canal to the River Severn at Coalport, was 7¾ miles long with a 2¾-mile branch. It contained three tunnels and three inclined planes including **The Hay inclined plane (SH12)**, 350 yards long, which took the canal boats down 207ft to the River Severn. Although nearly all traces of these canals have been obliterated by later development, a short length of the Shropshire Canal and the inclined plane at The Hay have been preserved within Blists Hill Industrial Museum site. Finally, the Shrewsbury Canal, engineered by Thomas Telford following the death of Josiah Clowes, connected the east Shropshire network to the town of Shrewsbury, a distance of 17 miles. This canal was notable since it included a series of locks at **Hadley Park (SH32)** with verti-cally rising guillotine gates and a short tunnel provided, unusually for that time, with a towpath. Where the canal crossed the River Tern at **Longdon upon Tern (SH17)**, Telford designed and built the first major cast-iron aqueduct in Britain, described in detail in Chapter 1 and the Gazetteer. The network was finally connected to the rest of the national canal network in 1835 with the opening of the Newport Branch of the Birmingham & Liverpool Junction Canal (discussed later in this chapter) at Wappenshall junction.

Another major development in the north-west of the region was the Ellesmere Canal (now part of the Shropshire Union network). The original intention of the promoters was for a canal linking the River Mersey at Ellesmere Port, southwards through the Welsh border hills and across the Rivers Dee and Ceriog, to the River Severn just above Shrewsbury. The Chief Engineer was William Jessop until 1800 with Thomas Telford as 'General Agent and Engineer'. Unfortunately the canal was never com-pleted as planned. Of the proposed main line only the sections between Weston Lullingfields (north-west of Shrewsbury) and Plas Kynaston (just north of the River Dee crossing) and between Chester and Ellesmere Port on the Mersey were built. To link the truncated main line of the canal

27 *Shropshire Canal at Blists Hill Museum.*

to the national network a long branch was built to join the existing Chester Canal and thus reach Chester. A further branch extended south-west to make a junction with the Montgomeryshire Canal when the eastern section of that canal was opened in 1797. The major features of the canal were the two great river crossings at **Chirk (SH10)** and Pontcysyllte, described in Chapter 1.

During his long career Thomas Telford was associated with a number of canal schemes in the West Midlands including the aforementioned Shrewsbury and Ellesmere canals. Later, as Britain's most eminent civil engineer of his day, he returned to the West Midlands to carry out three further projects.

In 1822 he was consulted by the Trent & Mersey Company on a solution to the problem of traffic congestion due to the old tunnel at **Harecastle (ST27)**. Thomas Telford, acting as consulting engineer to the company's Engineer, Joseph Potter, designed a new tunnel to run parallel with the old one and construction commenced in 1824 using 15 shafts. The tunnel, at 2,926 yards 46 yards longer than the original Brindley tunnel, was completed in

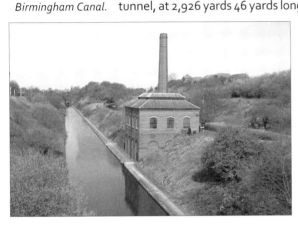

28 Smethwick Cutting showing old and new lines of the Birmingham Canal.

the spring of 1827, a construction period of less than three years compared with the nine years required to complete the first one 50 years earlier. The resident engineer was James Potter, Joseph's son, who was highly commended by Telford for his work here. It included a towpath through the tunnel, a feature of Telford's canal tunnels.

At about the same time, Telford was asked to advise the Birmingham Canal Company on the state of their main line of canal between Birmingham and Wolverhampton. In his report he described the existing canal as 'little better than a crooked ditch' and recommended large-scale improvements, the most spectacular of which was the driving of a 70ft-deep cutting past the summit level at Smethwick to bypass the six summit locks. The new canal was 40ft wide with towpaths on both sides and 20ft lower than the old line.

In several places new bridges were required to span the new cutting including **Winson Green Bridge (WM10)** and its near identical neighbour **Lee Bridge (WM10)**, both of 1826. **Galton Bridge (WM23)** of 1829 carries Roebuck Lane in Smethwick over the deepest part of the cutting. This bridge has now been bypassed and preserved. Also near Smethwick Telford had to carry the old **Engine Branch (WM22)** canal over his new line and to do so designed a very elegant aqueduct, unusual in carrying one canal over another. Telford's resident engineer was William Mackenzie. Mackenzie kept a detailed record of the excavation of the cutting by recording in coloured blocks the amount of excavation done each month. This record has survived and is deposited in the archives of the Institution of Civil Engineers and gives a fascinating insight into the progress of the work.

Telford's final project was the last major canal construction to be undertaken in Britain and marked his return to work in Shropshire where his career as a civil engineer had commenced some 39 years earlier. In 1826 he was appointed Engineer to the Birmingham & Liverpool Junction Canal Company to design and construct their new canal running 39½ miles from the end of the Chester Canal at Nantwich to a junction with the Staffordshire & Worcestershire Canal at Autherley junction near Wolverhampton. In designing the canal Telford used techniques which were much more applicable to railway engineering. He grouped the locks into flights with long level pounds in between, and used long straight alignments with deep cuttings and high embankments, a marked departure from earlier canal design.

Construction on this scale produced many remarkable engineering works but it also produced a string of problems. Cutting of the canal began in 1827 and a major feature is its earthworks. Typical of the cuttings is **Woodseaves Cutting (SH20)**, 2,900 yards long and up to 70ft deep with spectacular high bridges. **Cowley Cutting (ST11)** was intended to be a tunnel but severe ground problems forced the opening out of the tunnel and only a short length of tunnel was actually built.

The problems encountered in the construction of the deep steep-sided cuttings were severe enough but paled into insignificance in comparison with the problems Telford had to overcome at the one-mile-long **Shelmore Bank (ST13)**. This embankment, 1,900 yards long and in places some 60ft high, was made necessary by the need to divert the canal away from the estate of Lord Anson of Norbury Park. The soil from which the embankment was to be constructed proved to be unsuitable and settled continuously despite all efforts to contain it. The battle with the bank continued for six years and was only won after Telford's death.

29 *Birmingham & Liverpool junction Canal near Ellesmere.*

In February 1833 Telford had agreed to allow William Cubitt to deputise for him as he was now in poor health and he did not visit the canal again until March 1834 when he paid a last visit to Shelmore Bank, still uncompleted. The canal was finally opened throughout on 2 March 1835.

In 1830 the Liverpool & Manchester Railway was opened, which competed directly with the Bridgewater Canal for traffic between the two cities. The success of this and the other early railways lead to the widespread development of this rival system of transport. Inevitably the inland waterway network suffered and many of the canal and river navigation companies eventually passed into the hands of railway companies. A slow decline of traffic and revenue took place with consequent lack of maintenance leading to further loss of traffic. However, much of the national network of inland waterways remained intact. One notable example of this survival is the majority of the extensive network of canals in the Black Country around Birmingham. During the period of canal building, up to about 1830, most of the new industry had developed along the banks of the new canals. Thus, even when the railway arrived after 1838, the canals continuted to be used as a local distribution system. Many interchange basins were built at which goods were transferred between railway and canal, being taken to the final destination by boat. **Chillington Wharf (WM30)**, near Wolverhampton, is the last remaining basin largely in its original state with a canal basin flanked by railway sidings. The sidings are laid at a level below the canal water level thus enabling goods to be easily exchanged between railway wagon and boat across a narrow wharf.

Following the Second World War, freight carried on waterways declined rapidly with a few exceptions (the network of waterways north of the Humber being an example) but the system has undergone a remarkable transformation in recent years, becoming a major leisure facility with large and increasing numbers of privately owned and hire craft using the system each year. Thus, the future of the nation's inland waterways seems assured for future generations.

This chapter covers the history and development of the railway system of the West Midlands region. Although the railway era is normally considered to have started with the opening of the Stockton & Darlington Railway in 1825 and the Liverpool & Manchester Railway in 1830, there were many earlier tramways and railways in the West Midlands region. Many of these were built as feeders to the comprehensive network of canals which had developed in the West Midlands, considered in detail in Chapter 2. These railways were normally short in length, of fairly simple construction and usually horse-drawn, and were used to bring goods from a local coal mine, quarry or factory to a canal-side wharf for transhipment into canal boats for onward carriage. As an illustration of this type of early railway, two typical examples in the region will be considered in detail.

The first of these was the Stratford & Moreton Tramway, a horse-drawn tramway running 16 miles between the Stratford Canal at Stratford-upon-Avon and Moreton-in-Marsh with a branch to Shipston on Stour from Darlingscott. The railway opened as early as 1826, four years before the opening of the Liverpool & Manchester Railway and only one year after the opening of the Stockton & Darlington Railway. The tramway was intended to be the first part of a much greater scheme for the Central Junction Railway or Tramroad proposed by William James to run from Stratford-upon-Avon to London. (A similar scheme to build a Central Junction Canal between Stratford-upon-Avon and the River Thames had been proposed in 1810 by John Rennie.) At Stratford the tramway commenced at the basin where the Stratford-upon-Avon Canal met the River Avon. Here goods were to be transhipped from canal and river boats to the tramway for onward carriage to the south. The original intention of its promoters, led by William James, was to use steam locomotives on the tramway and to this end consultations were held with George Stephenson. The Engineer for the construction of the tramway was John Urpeth Rastrick (see Chapter 1). Unfortunately a clause was inserted into its second Act of Parliament, needed to raise additional finance, preventing the use of steam locomotives for the six miles of tramway alongside the turnpike road south of Stratford-upon-Avon. This restricted the railway to a horse-drawn tramway which remained until 1889 when the section from Moreton-in-Marsh to Shipston on Stour was re-laid by the Great Western Railway, by this time the owner of the line, as a steam engine operated railway. The northern section of the line remained horse-drawn and was last used about 1904. In 1918 the track was lifted for war scrap but the Moreton-in-Marsh to Shipston on Stour section remained in use for freight traffic until May 1960.

William James was born 13 June 1771 at Henley in Arden and by the age of 25 he was referring to himself as a Land Agent and Surveyor. He bought his first share in the Stratford Canal in 1793 and in 1799 he was appointed Land Agent to the Earl of Warwick. In 1802 he travelled north to inspect canals and railways and met the Duke of Bridgewater. He had become Chairman of the Stratford Canal Company and in 1813 he purchased the Upper Avon Navigation. However, he became convinced that railways were the future for transport and for the rest of his life he was associated with many railway projects. In 1819-20 James surveyed the line for his 'Central Junction Railway' from Stratford to London via Moreton-in-Marsh, Oxford, Thame and Uxbridge, of which the Stratford to Moreton section was to have been the first phase. Stratford was to be the transshipment point between canal and railway, reflecting James's interests in the navigations based on Stratford. Unfortunately James was imprisoned for debt in 1823 and although he took the post of clerk to the tramway company on his release from prison, he was removed from the post in 1826 and retired to Bodmin in Cornwall, where he died on 10 March 1837.

A second example of a canal-associated railway is the Shutt End Railway which opened in 1829. This line was promoted by Lord Dudley and served to carry coal from his colliery at Shutt End near Stourbridge to Ashwood Basin on the Staffordshire & Worcestershire Canal, a distance of three miles. Its main claim to fame is that it used a locomotive – the *Agenoria* – for the two-mile level section between its two inclined planes. The *Agenoria* was built at Stourbridge by John Urpeth Rastrick, one of the founders of the Stourbridge firm of Foster, Rastrick & Partners, who also built the *Stourbridge Lion*, which was exported to the United States and became one of the first locomotives to run there. The *Agenoria* has survived and may be seen in the National Railway Museum. The Shutt End Railway later became part of the Pensnett Railway, an extensive private railway system owned by Lord Dudley and associated with Round Oak steelworks.

Although the earliest modern inter-city railway, the Liverpool & Manchester which opened in 1830, was not in the West Midlands region, the West Midlands was the target, as with the canals before them, for several of the next generation of railway lines to be developed in Britain.

30 *William James.*

As has been described, by about 1825, the date of the opening of the Stockton & Darlington Railway and the beginning of the modern railway era, the West Midlands already possessed a modern transport system in the form of canals with their associated feeder railways. A major influence on the way in which railways developed in the area was that the coming of the canal system had already sparked off a major development of industry, especially in the area between Birmingham and Wolverhampton, and many of the factories had developed along the banks of the canals which served them.

The success of the Liverpool & Manchester Railway provoked a rash of railway development proposals and it is significant that two of the first lines ended in Birmingham. These two lines were the London & Birmingham Railway and the Grand Junction Railway. The Grand Junction Railway was to be a link between the Liverpool & Manchester line and Birmingham and thus to connect the West Midlands (and London via the London & Birmingham Railway) to both the port of Liverpool and to Manchester. These two railways were authorised by Acts of Parliament on the same day, 6 May 1833.

The man most closely associated with the early development of railways in Britain is George Stephenson. Stephenson did not invent the steam locomotive; if anyone deserves the credit it is Richard Trevithick, whose locomotive of 1804, which ran briefly on the Penydarren Tramroad in South Wales, is generally regarded as having made the first successful journey by steam. However, George Stephenson was important in the development of the steam locomotive and the steam-operated railway, and he was the prime figure in the development of most of the early lines. He was the Engineer for both the Stockton & Darlington and the Liverpool & Manchester Railways, but in the West Midlands the most influential person was George's son, Robert Stephenson. Robert was closely involved with his father in the planning of the London & Birmingham Railway for which he was appointed the sole Engineer.

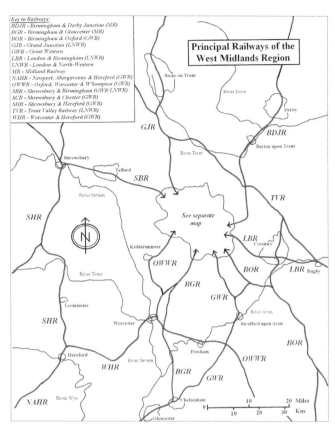

Principal Railways of the West Midlands Region

Key to Railways:
BDJR - Birmingham & Derby Junction (MR)
BGR - Birmingham & Gloucester (MR)
BOR - Birmingham & Oxford (GWR)
GJR - Grand Junction (LNWR)
GWR - Great Western
LBR - London & Birmingham (LNWR)
LNWR - London & North-Western
MR - Midland Railway
NAHR - Newport, Abergavenny & Hereford (GWR)
OWWR - Oxford, Worcester & W'hampton (GWR)
SBR - Shrewsbury & Birmingham (GWR LNWR)
SCR - Shrewsbury & Chester (GWR)
SHR - Shrewsbury & Hereford (GWR)
TVR - Trent Valley Railway (GWR)
WHR - Worcester & Hereford (GWR)

31 (Above) Loco-motive Agenoria, Shutt End Railway.

32 (Above right) The principal railways of the West Midlands region.

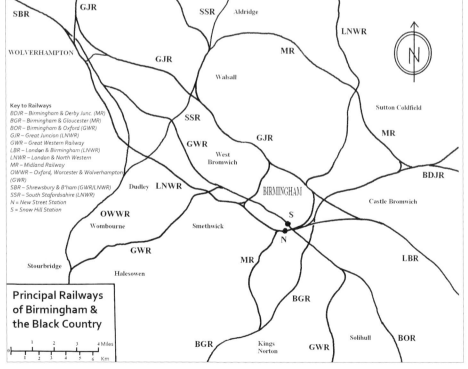

Key to Railways
BDJR – Birmingham & Derby Junc. (MR)
BGR – Birmingham & Gloucester (MR)
BOR – Birmingham & Oxford (GWR)
GJR – Great Juncion (LNWR)
GWR – Great Western Railway
LBR – London & Birmingham (LNWR)
LNWR – London & North Western
MR – Midland Railway
OWWR – Oxford, Worcester & Wolverhampton (GWR)
SBR – Shrewsbury & B'ham (GWR/LNWR)
SSR – South Stafordsahire (LNWR)
N = New Street Station
S = Snow Hill Station

Principal Railways of Birmingham & the Black Country

33 (Right) The principal railways of Birmingham and the Black Country.

34 *Trevithick's Pen-y-Darren locomotive.*

35 *George Stephenson.*

Robert Stephenson was born near Newcastle upon Tyne on 16 October 1803. He was educated in Newcastle between 1814 and 1819 then apprenticed to Nicholas Wood at Killingworth Colliery, where his father worked as an engine-wright. In 1822 he studied for six months at Edinburgh University before working for his father, who had established the firm of Robert Stephenson and Company. In 1824 he departed for Colombia in South America to supervise the re-opening of gold and silver mines there but returned in 1827 to resume work alongside his father. George and Robert designed the *Rocket* locomotive, the victor in the Rainhill Trials on the newly built Liverpool & Manchester Railway which helped to assure the future of the steam locomotive on the growing network of railways. For the newly promoted London & Birmingham Railway both George and Robert carried out the survey work but following the passing of the Act for the railway in 1833 Robert was appointed Chief Engineer, a job he successfully completed despite many difficulties encountered during the building of the line. Subsequently he was involved with many railway projects both in Britain and abroad. He designed and built many famous structures including the Britannia Tubular Bridge over the Menai Straits, the High Level Bridge at Newcastle and the Royal Border Bridge. Other tubular bridges were built to his design in Canada (the Victoria Bridge over the St Lawrence river) and Egypt. By 1859 his health was failing and he died on 12 October 1859. He was one of only two civil engineers to be buried in Westminster Abbey, the other being Thomas Telford.

The Grand Junction, with easier terrain, was the first to be completed, opening to a new terminus in Birmingham at Curzon Street on 4 July 1837. It was 82½ miles in length. The route of the railway started outside this region with a junction at Newton le Willows on the Liverpool & Manchester Railway, from whence it ran south via Warrington, Crewe and Stafford to Birmingham. One interesting aspect of the route followed by the Grand Junction Railway, and which probably relates to the state of development at the time, was that it did not pass through Wolverhampton; instead it described a long curve to approach Birmingham from the north-east (now the line via Aston and Perry Barr). The line was laid out by George Stephenson and John Rastrick with Joseph Locke as assistant, but there were difficulties between George Stephenson and Locke and the responsibility for the construction was split between them, with Locke becoming responsible for the southern half of the project. In August 1835 George Stephenson withdrew and Locke became Chief Engineer for the whole line. There were no great technical difficulties with the construction of the line although there were several viaducts, including a seven-span viaduct over the River Penk at **Penkridge (ST23)** and Lawley Street viaduct in Birmingham with 28 arches.

36 *(Below) Robert Stephenson.*

37 *(Below right) Joseph Locke.*

Joseph Locke was born on 9 August 1805 at Attercliffe. In 1823 he was articled to George Stephenson at Newcastle and assisted him on the surveys for the Liverpool & Manchester Railway. He resigned from the Liverpool & Manchester Railway in 1832 following a dispute with Stephenson and thereafter worked on his own account. Following the building of the Grand Junction Railway, he was engineer for many railway projects including the London & Southampton Railway, the Lancaster & Carlisle Railway with John Errington, and several lines in Scotland. He was active in the building of railways abroad, particularly in France where he engineered the lines between Paris and Rouen (1841-3) and Rouen to Le Havre (1843), as well as lines in Holland and Spain. In these projects he frequently worked with Thomas Brassey, the famous railway contractor. He died aged 55 in September 1860.

The building of the London & Birmingham Railway was a much more difficult undertaking. The line started at Euston Station in London (the original terminus was to have been at Camden but a late alteration extended it to Euston). From London the line crossed the Chiltern Hills by way of the great cutting at Tring, crossed the Ouse valley at Wolverton then on to Bletchley, Weedon, Rugby and Coventry. The most difficult works on the line were the long, deep cutting at Roade in Northamptonshire with its massive brick retaining walls, and the 2,416-yard tunnel through the ridge of high ground east of Rugby. The railway opened from London to Denbigh Hall and from Birmingham to Rugby in April 1838, but the severe difficulties in completing Roade Cutting and Kilsby Tunnel delayed the complete opening of the line until 17 September 1838.

In Birmingham both railways had terminal stations side by side at **Curzon Street (WM2)**. For the London & Birmingham Railway, architect Philip Hardwick designed imposing terminal buildings at each end of the line. Euston, dominated by its entrance Doric-style propylaeum, contrasted with the Ionic-style columns at the entrance to the station at Curzon Street.

38 *Roade cutting looking north. Note brick retaining walls.*

The passenger train services provided by these early railways were infrequent, slow and expensive. On the London & Birmingham Railway in 1838 there were nine trains daily each way, the fastest, the mail trains, taking five hours at an average speed of 22½ m.p.h., the slowest taking 8¾ hours. Fares were high, the figures for 1842 being £1 2s. 6d. first-class single and 14s. third-class, at a time when wages for a building worker was about 4s. per day. The locomotives were small four-wheeled engines and the passenger coaches were of a fairly simple variety, being basically road coach bodies on four-wheeled wagons. Both for the carriage of passengers and freight the railways had immediate advantages over the canal system. Firstly they were much faster; secondly they were able to offer the beginnings of a national network since, at least in the early days, the railways had a common track gauge enabling all carriages and wagons to run on the lines of the various companies.

Even before the completion of these two railways, the success, both commercial and financial, of the early railways was well known and from that time railway promotion became a popular activity. Birmingham rapidly became one of the hubs of the national railway system, although there was no overall planning for a national network. As previously with the canals, most railway promotion was done on a local basis, with lines proposed to connect two population centres with little thought being given to other developments. The emergence of a national network came about almost by accident by the joining up of these largely local schemes although a few individuals, including the notorious George Hudson, took a wider view.

The next two railways to head for Birmingham were from the south and east. The Birmingham & Gloucester Railway was authorised in 1836 and opened on 17 August 1841. The line was engineered by Captain W.S. Moorsom and ran from Gloucester via Cheltenham and Bromsgrove to a temporary terminus at Camp Hill, then shortly afterwards by a link with the London & Birmingham to Curzon Street. It included the notorious **Lickey Incline (WR5)** by which the railway ascended from the valley of the River Severn at Bromsgrove to the Birmingham plateau. With a total rise of about 300ft over a distance of only two miles, the incline has a gradient of 1 in 37.7 (2.7 per cent). Whereas at this time such a steep incline would normally have been used with stationary engines to haul trains up the bank, Lickey Incline was planned from the outset for locomotive operation. Initially, special locomotives were imported from the United States of America to pull trains up the incline but after a short while banking engines were developed locally by James McConnell, the superintendent of the line. Until the end of steam traction in the 1960s, most ascending trains required banking assistance. At this time the railway ran into Birmingham via Kings Heath and Moseley. The present link from Kings Norton to New Street via Five Ways was not built at this time – more of this later.

39 *A typical first-and second-class carriage of the early railways.*

The second line, the Birmingham & Derby Junction Railway, was also authorised in 1836 and ran from Derby to Birmingham via Burton upon Trent and Tamworth. The original intention, to run direct to Birmingham, was changed and at Whitacre the line swung south via the nominally independent Stonebridge Railway to join the London & Birmingham at Hampton in Arden. The junction faced towards London and all Birmingham & Derby trains had to reverse at

Hampton in Arden and run to Curzon Street along the London & Birmingham's tracks. This railway opened on 12 August 1839. Relations with the London & Birmingham were unsatisfactory and the Birmingham & Derby soon resolved to build their own line direct to Birmingham and on 10 February 1842 they opened a new line from Whitacre to their own terminus at Lawley Street, adjacent to Curzon Street. For three years, the Stonebridge Railway was an important link in the railway chain, being on the most direct route from London to York via the London & Birmingham, the Birmingham & Derby junction, the North Midland and the York & North Midland Railways. The opening of the Midland Counties Railway between Rugby and Derby in 1840 gave a more direct route between London and York and reduced the status of the Stonebridge Railway to a minor branch line. It was closed to through traffic in 1939 and, after being used as a long siding for many years, was finally closed and most of the track lifted in 1951.

The 1840s were a time of important mergers and amalgamations. In May 1844 the Birmingham & Derby junction was merged with other lines to form the Midland Railway and in 1846 the Midland also took over the Birmingham & Gloucester. In January 1846 the London & Birmingham, Grand Junction and Liverpool & Manchester Railway merged to form the London & North Western Railway (LNWR) and thus were formed the two great railway companies which, together with the Great Western Railway (considered in more detail later), were to dominate the railway scene in the West Midlands until 1923.

By the early 1840s, all railways entering Birmingham did so from the east and consequently there was at Curzon Street a complex of three stations, the London & Birmingham, the Grand Junction and the Birmingham & Derby, at different levels. In addition, both the Birmingham and Gloucester from the south and the Manchester & Birmingham from the north (via the Grand Junction) had trains running into Curzon Street. All this caused great congestion in the area. An additional problem was that the Curzon Street site was (as with most city stations of the time) on the fringes of the built-up area and access to the town was through narrow and inadequate streets. A new station in Birmingham was clearly needed.

The matter was considered by a Select Committee of Parliament and two sites for new stations were considered. These were at Navigation Street (later to be known as New Street) and Snow Hill. Strong arguments were put forward for both sites by the rival promoters. The area occupied by New Street was largely poor-quality property which the city was anxious to be rid of, whereas Snow Hill was nearer the commercial centre of the town. Eventually both sites were given Parliamentary approval with compulsory purchase powers in 1846. The New Street site was developed by the LNWR with the Midland having running powers and sharing the station. The short extension of ⅞ mile from Curzon Street (via Grand Junction and Proof House junction) was engineered by Robert Stephenson and the new station was formally opened in 1854. New Street station was extensively rebuilt in the 1960s in conjunction with the electrification of the West Coast Main Line but recent increases in rail traffic have caused operational difficulties at the station and a further rebuild is now proposed.

The early move to New Street ensured the survival for posterity of the Curzon Street station building, which languished firstly as an excursion station and subsequently as an obscure goods station until recent years when the building was renovated and has found other uses.

The Snow Hill site was to be shared by overlapping powers granted to two newly promoted companies – the Birmingham & Oxford (B&O) and the Birmingham, Wolverhampton & Dudley railways. These two companies quickly agreed to amalgamate and sell or lease their lines to the Great Western, which had opened its line from Didcot to Oxford in 1844. The Great Western had been built by Brunel on the broad gauge of 7ft ¼in and the Great Western's ambitions extended far beyond the West Midlands. The sale to the GWR was completed in 1848 despite the ingenious opposition of the LNWR. For example, in 1847 the Euston faction had managed to acquire 80 per cent of the shareholding of the Birmingham & Oxford company and tried to enlarge the Board of Directors so as to include people sympathetic to the LNWR's point of view. However, this move was successfully resisted by the B&O and the GWR, who had already agreed a lease, and the LNWR action was held to be *ultra vires*. The lines were built and Snow Hill station opened in 1852, thus bringing the broad gauge into the heart of the Midlands for the first time.

The acrimony between the LNWR and the GWR had one consequence which may still be seen today. As a part of the Act for the Birmingham & Oxford line there was to be a connecting link between the B&O and the LNWR just outside New Street station and the GWR started work on a ½-mile line north of Duddesdon. A short length of viaduct was completed as far as the boundary of LNWR property. However, the LNWR refused to surrender the land required for the link and the project was left unfinished. The unused Duddesdon viaduct may still be seen today, left in isolation for over 150 years.

In the late 1840s there were two rival proposals to drive westwards from Birmingham towards Wolverhampton and the west. The LNWR proposed a line, the Birmingham, Wolverhampton & Stour Valley Railway, even today known misleadingly as the Stour Valley line although the Stour Valley section towards Kidderminster was never built. This was to run direct from New Street to Wolverhampton with a connection to the Grand Junction line to Stafford at Bushbury. This would have the effect of rectifying the omission of Wolverhampton and the intervening rapidly developing area from the original Grand Junction route. The second line was the Shrewsbury & Birmingham Railway (S&B) or more accurately the Shrewsbury and Wolverhampton railway since it only had running powers over the Stour Valley line from Wolverhampton to Birming-ham. Unfortunately the S&B had concluded a traffic agreement with the GWR and this inflamed the LNWR, who were determined to prevent their great rival from getting a foothold in New Street. The Shrewsbury & Birmingham was completed by 1849 to a temporary station at Wolverhampton and intended to run its trains into New Street via the LNWR Stour Valley line. By 1851 the LNWR had completed the Stour Valley line but refused to open it to prevent the S&B trains from gaining access to Birmingham. After legal and parliamentary moves to try and enforce its running powers, the S&B tried to force the issue by running a train from Wolverhampton High Level station to New Street. The LNWR in reply blocked the line near Wolverhampton with a locomotive. Matters were resolved eventually and in July 1852 the Stour Valley line was fully opened. However, the GWR-inspired Birmingham, Wolverhampton & Dudley (BW&D) line to Wolverhampton was finished in 1854 and this enabled the S&B to run through to Snow Hill via Stafford Road and Cannock Road junctions, through Wolverhampton Low Level Station. The GWR line from Birmingham to Stafford Road junction was mixed broad and standard gauge and this was the furthest point north reached by the broad gauge, the broad gauge rail being removed in 1869.

In fact, the BW&D did not reach Wolverhampton directly since the last mile of the line to Wolverhampton (Low Level) passed over the tracks of another GWR-inspired line – the Oxford, Worcester & Wolverhampton Railway. The OWWR (or 'Old Worse and Worse' as it became known as a result of its appalling service in its early days) started at a junction with the GWR just north of Oxford and proceeded west and then north via Evesham, Worcester and Dudley to a low-level station in Wolverhampton, and it was at Priestfield junction that it was joined by the BW&D line from Snow Hill. The OWWR was notoriously involved in the 'Gauge War' of 1844-54. It was planned as a mixed broad and standard gauge line but fell out with the GWR during construction and proposed to abandon the broad gauge and strike up a partnership with the LNWR and the Midland. It was finally compelled by the GWR to complete the laying of the broad-gauge rail but the broad gauge was never used (except of course for the short section from Priestfield to Wolverhampton) and most of the broad-gauge rail had been taken up by 1858. One of the OWWR's more notorious incidents was the tragic accident in August 1858 between Round Oak and Brettell Lane in which 14 people were killed and more than 50 injured when part of an excursion train ran away backwards down the steep gradient there and collided with a following train.

One interesting aspect of the construction of the OWWR was the use of timber viaducts, a speciality of Isambard Brunel, the line's Engineer. The view of Hoo Brook Viaduct looks conventional enough but a closer inspection of the abutments reveals the abutments of the original timber viaduct, which was later replaced by the existing brick structure.

Fig. 41 shows in detail the complex pattern of railways in the Wolverhampton area which finally emerged. The short length of line between Cannock Road junction and Bushbury junction is of interest because it is said that the only passenger trains to use it were the special trains conveying

40 *Hoo Brook Viaduct showing abutments of old timber viaduct.*

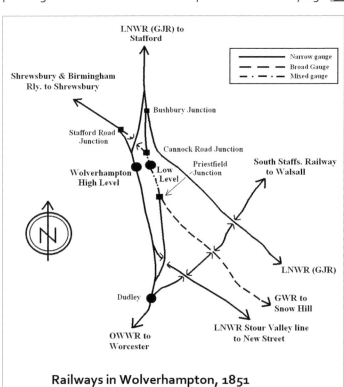

Railways in Wolverhampton, 1851

41 *Map of railways in the Wolverhampton area.*

42   *A Severn Valley Railway train at Highley station.*

43   *The west portal of Shugborough Tunnel on the Trent Valley Railway.*

Queen Victoria to Balmoral from Windsor, the line forming a convenient exchange point between the GWR and the LNWR routes.

In the west of the region railways were developed leading south and south-west as well as lines reaching westwards into Wales. Most of this development was in the hands of the GWR and its associated companies with lines from the OWWR at Kidderminster to Shrewsbury (1862) and westwards to Tenbury Wells (1864). From Worcester lines ran south-west to Great Malvern and Hereford and west in stages to Leominster (1874-97). Part of the Kidderminster to Shrewsbury route is now the highly successful Severn Valley Railway which preserves the atmosphere of steam traction on a rural branch line.

In 1845 construction began of a new shorter line to the north for trains not required to stop at Birmingham. This was the Trent Valley Railway which runs for just over 50 miles between the London & Birmingham Railway at Rugby north-west to the Grand Junction line at Stafford via Nuneaton and Tamworth. The Chief Engineer for the line was Thomas Gooch with Robert Stephenson and George Bidder also associated with the design. The line was opened in 1847, by which time the railway, although initially promoted by an independent company, had become part of the LNWR.

One notable engineering work on the line is the 774-yard **Shugborough Tunnel (ST26)** beneath the grounds of Shugborough Hall with its ornate castellated portals designed to blend in with the landscape of the park. Originally built as a double-track line, it was widened in the late 19th century to three and four tracks in places and has very recently been upgraded almost completely to a four track layout as part of the West Coast Main Line's modernisation.

By 1855 the major elements of the Birmingham and Wolverhampton network were in place. To complete the picture it is only necessary to consider three further lines – the South Staffordshire Railway, the direct link to Stourbridge and the Birmingham West Suburban Railway.

The South Staffordshire Railway was a line right through the heart of the Black Country, starting in the south at a junction with the OWWR at Dudley and running north via Walsall, Brownhills and Lichfield to a junction with the Midland Railway at Wychnor. This line opened in 1849. Later, in 1858, the South Staffs. moved into the Cannock coalfield with a line to Cannock from Walsall, later extended to Rugeley where it made a junction with the Trent Valley cut-off line.

The direct link between Birmingham and Stourbridge started life as a branch from the OWWR at Stourbridge to Cradley in 1863, then to Old Hill in 1866. This was later extended northwards in 1867 to connect with the LNWR Stour Valley line via Smethwick junction and Galton junction, then it crossed the Stour Valley line at what is today Smethwick Galton Bridge two-level station, and joined the GWR line to Snow Hill at Handsworth junction.

In 1862 a connection was made by the Midland Railway between the Birmingham & Derby line and the Birmingham & Gloucester, thus allowing traffic to run directly between Derby and Gloucester without reversing at New Street for the first time in over 20 years.

In 1876 the Birmingham West Suburban Railway was opened as a long branch line running northwards from the Midland Railway's Birmingham & Gloucester line at Lifford to a separate terminus at Granville Street, just to the west of the Worcester & Birmingham Canal at Gas Street. For much of its route it followed the bank of the Worcester & Birmingham Canal, giving a heavily curved alignment. In 1881 the logical extension to New Street was authorised and the line passed into the hands of the Midland Railway. In order to construct the line into New Street, much tunnelling was required and the canal had to be diverted, requiring the construction of **Holliday Street Aqueduct (WM7)**. This was an attractive purchase for the Midland as it enabled their southbound trains to call at Birmingham without having to reverse at New Street, and from then on this became the main Midland route into Birmingham from the south and the original section of the Birmingham & Gloucester from Lifford to New Street became of secondary importance.

In 1894 the Birmingham & North Warwickshire Railway (B&NWR) was authorised. This line was projected privately as a direct route from Birmingham to Stratford-upon-Avon but did not make any progress until 1900, when the GWR took over and built the line in its present form from a junction with the GWR main line at Tyseley direct to a junction with the Great Western's Hatton to Stratford line at Bearley. It opened in 1907. This route, together with a line between Honeybourne and Cheltenham, opened in 1906, gave the Great Western a new direct route to Bristol largely independent of the Midland Railway. The B&NWR also gave Birmingham its last new terminus as, instead of running into Snow Hill, trains on this line could be terminated at Moor Street, a cramped new station just outside Snow Hill Tunnel, famous for its traverser at the end of the platform roads. This station has recently undergone a restoration to its original splendour.

In the west of the region there were several further important developments which together provided a north-south link from Crewe in the north to Hereford and South Wales. In 1846 the Shrewsbury & Chester Railway was established by amalgamating two earlier companies. The line from Chester to Shrewsbury was constructed with Henry Robertson as Engineer and Brassey, Mackenzie and Stephenson as contractors. It opened in stages, being opened throughout in October 1848 to a temporary station in Shrewsbury, the new joint station being opened in June 1849. Robertson was faced with crossing the same two deep river valleys of the River Dee, near Llangollen, and the River Ceriog at Chirk that had confronted Thomas Telford and William Jessop during the construction of the Ellesmere Canal some 45 years earlier. Two large viaducts were constructed. Cefn Viaduct (SJ 285412), over the River Dee with 21 stone and brick arches, a total length of 1,508ft and a greatest height of 148ft, was claimed to be the longest viaduct in Britain at the time of its building. Over the valley of the River Ceriog **Chirk Viaduct (SH10)**, an 846ft-long timber and stone viaduct, was built with a maximum height of 106ft, rebuilt in stone in 1859.

The second link in the Crewe to Hereford route was the Shrewsbury & Hereford Railway, authorised in 1846 for a 51-mile line, again with Henry Robertson as engineer and Thomas Brassey as contractor. The line opened from Shrewsbury to Ludlow in April 1852 and onwards to Hereford in December 1853. Unusually, Thomas Brassey not only built but also worked the line until 1862 when the railway was leased jointly to the Great Western and the London & North Western Railways.

From here on the story of the railways in the centre and east of the region is one of the proliferation of minor branch lines and interconnecting links. By 1906 the railway network of the West Midlands had reached its greatest extent and from then onwards a slow decline set in and recent developments will be considered shortly.

It is interesting to examine the way in which the relationships between the railways and canals developed in Birmingham and the Black Country. In most parts of the country, the arrival of a railway on a parallel route normally spelt a lingering death sentence for the canal. The more astute canal companies sold out to the rival railway company but those that did not generally foundered after a period of toll-rate cutting rapidly depleting their financial resources. However, even today, most of the canal network established by the 1830s has remained largely intact. The reason for this is that, as described in Chapter 2, much of the early industry in the area was established along the banks of the existing canals. When the railways arrived on the scene, they were happy to co-exist with the canals, the canals providing the local distribution network direct to the factory doors with the railways providing the long-distance connections. Even as late as 1949 the Birmingham canal network was still carrying 1,220,000 tons per annum. Its demise was brought about by competition from road-based transport, not railways, and by 1964 the traffic had fallen to 340,000 tons and has now effectively ceased.

As with the canals, the region's railway network has remained largely intact despite the intense competition from road transport, both for passenger and freight transport. The main casualty has been the Great Western line through the area, since this was a direct duplication of the old LNWR route. Most direct services to London and the north-west were transferred to the LNWR routes in the 1960s with the electrification of the London & Birmingham and Grand Junction routes by 1967. After a period of decline, Snow Hill Station was finally closed in 1972, the remaining services on the old GWR line to the south being terminated at Moor Street or running into New Street via a connecting line at Bordesley junction. Trains from the Stourbridge line were diverted into New Street along the Stour Valley line from Galton junction, and Snow Hill Station was demolished. However, this was not to be the end of the Great Western route.

A new station has been built on the site of Snow Hill that now acts as a terminus or through station for the Chiltern Railways services running south to London Marylebone via Leamington Spa, Banbury and the Bicester Cut-off line, thus forming an alternative to the London & Birmingham route. The track bed northwards from Snow Hill, having languished unused but luckily protected from development for many years, has also been re-opened, together with a revival of the connection to the Stourbridge line at Smethwick, enabling Stourbridge line trains to run through to Snow Hill and thus relieve the overloaded New Street of some of its traffic. At Galton Bridge station there is a convenient passenger interchange between the New Street to Wolverhampton line (low level) and the Stourbridge to Snow Hill route (high level).

The old GWR route between Snow Hill and Wolverhampton has also been used for the first section of the Midland Metro tramway project, with further extensions proposed. New stations have been opened on the route and some old ones re-opened with the aim of encouraging commuters to leave their cars and return to the railways.

What lessons can this history teach us? With railways, as with the canals before them, development proceeded in distinct stages. First came the pioneering lines, projected where a need for transport was clearly perceived by their promoters. Later came the 'mania' during which railways were projected as purely speculative ventures, with little regard being paid to the traffic potential. The industrial west midlands seems to have been largely spared this type of railway promotion but it did suffer from rivalling companies developing parallel routes in some places.

The grouping of the railways into four major companies in 1923 left the area mainly in the hands of the London, Midland & Scottish Railway, the inheritors of the LNWR and the Midland, but with a significant GWR presence in its line through Birmingham and Wolverhampton to Birkenhead. This reduced, but not entirely eliminated, the competitive element, but nationalisation in 1948 removed this aspect altogether. Rationalisation of the competing routes was inevitable and it was the Great Western route that was sacrificed.

The region contains England's only inland cliff railway. This is **Bridgnorth Cliff Railway (SH5)**, which enables passengers to ascend from the Lower Town by the River Severn to the Upper Town 111ft higher without recourse to a lengthy flight of steps. It was opened in 1892 and is still in daily operation.

Following the success of the preservation and operation in 1951 of the Tal-y-Llyn Railway on the Welsh coast, railway preservation has developed rapidly and the West Midlands region is the site of several lines. Most of the preservation companies operate with a mainly volunteer staff although some of the more extensive lines employ full time staff in technical and managerial roles. The most prominent is the Severn Valley Railway which carries passengers between Kidderminster and **Bridgnorth (SH6)** along the route of the original Severn Valley Railway, opened in 1862. At Bridgnorth the railway has established a locomotive depot and extensive workshop facilities. The Gloucester-shire & Warwickshire Railway currently runs between Toddington in Gloucestershire and Cheltenham Racecourse station and has plans to extend northwards up through Warwickshire to Broadway. In Telford is the Telford Steam Railway and at Chasewater, near Brownhills, is the Chasewater Railway situated in the country park.

Finally in our study of transport modes, we return to the earliest form of transport – the road. From the earliest of times man has travelled on land. In ancient times this would be by means of the ancient track ways which crossed the country. These usually kept as far as possible to the high ground as most lower ground would be thickly wooded and difficult to pass. Examples of these ancient routes still remain, notable examples being the Ridgeway along the Berkshire-Wiltshire Downs and the Pilgrim Way from Salisbury Plain into Kent. More local to this volume was one running along the Jurassic ridge of the Cotswolds. Where the route was forced to cross low-lying wetter areas it is likely that simple wooden track ways were built. One of these was unearthed recently in the Somerset Levels and dated from about 2,500 B.C. However, by the very nature of the materials used, little traces of these now remain.

With the development of wheeled transport there would be a need for better routes, avoiding the ridge ways with their steep inclines, and there is some evidence of simple road works with embanking and ditching for a drier and hence more stable surface. However, little progress was made in the science of road building until the coming of the Romans to Britain.

By the time of their occupation of the province of Britannia in A.D. 43 the Romans were already experienced road builders and their legacy can still be seen today. In Britain, as in the other parts of their empire, they provided a high-quality road network, originally for military purposes. There are known to have been about 7,500 miles of Roman roads in Britain with possibly another 2,000 miles which have not been found. The Romans were the first to introduce a form of scientific approach to road building, with three primary requirements still in use today. These were, firstly, a well-drained foundation for the road; secondly, a strong road pavement (a term used by highway engineers to denote the traffic-bearing structure); and thirdly a smooth, hard-wearing surface. In Roman times these were achieved by providing a raised mound of soil (the 'agger') to lift the road above the surrounding wet soil, with side ditches where necessary for additional drainage. On the agger a foundation of larger stones would be laid, covered with smaller stones with a camber or slope to aid drainage of the surface. In some cases, probably on the more important routes, the final road surface was composed of paving stones but more often was a firm bed of gravel. The famous feature of Roman roads is their direct route with long straight sections between changes of alignment usually at high points from which the Roman surveyors could set out the road's direction. For river crossings the Romans used fords or built bridges, probably of timber but often on masonry piers. Substantial remains of Roman bridges can be seen at Piercebridge near Darlington on the line of Dere Street and at Chollerford near Hexham where the road running parallel to Hadrian's Wall crossed the River Tyne, both well outside the scope of this volume.

The density of the Roman road network is impressive, all the major Roman towns being linked by major roads with a system of less important routes between. The West Midlands was crossed by several of these major routes. The Fosse Way, which linked Lincoln (*Lindum*) south west to Exeter (*Isca*) still forms, for much of its route, the alignment of a modern road. Watling Street, running from Dover (*Dubris*) and London (*Londinium*) north-westwards to Wroxeter (*Viroconium*) near Shrewsbury is also followed for most of its route by the modern A2 and A5 roads. It intersects the Fosse Way at High Cross (*Venonae*) near Hinckley on the border between Leicestershire and Warwickshire. Other Roman roads are usually traceable on a map by virtue of their direct alignment, 43

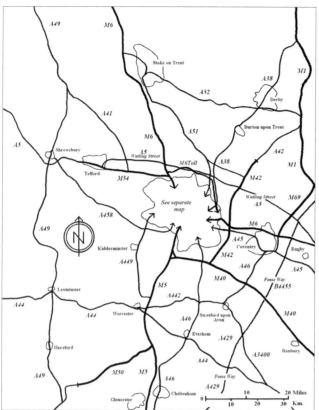

44 *Abutment of Roman Bridge at Piercebridge.*

45 *Road map of West Midlands.*

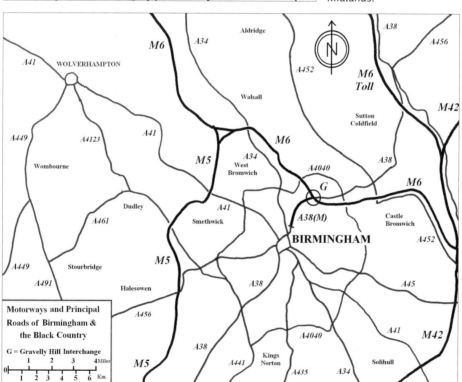

Motorways and Principal Roads of Birmingham & the Black Country

G = Gravelly Hill Interchange

46 *Map of Birmingham roads.*

this region including routes from Lichfield to Bourton on the Water (Ryknild Street), Hereford to Shrewsbury and many more.

Following the end of the Roman occupation in A.D. 410, the legacy of the great Roman road system gradually fell into disrepair and, apart from some military road building in Scotland from about 1725 and some causeways built in the fens and across major river valleys, no more metalled roads were built in Britain until the turnpike movement of the 18th century. Maintenance of roads became a local responsibility with common law requiring all inhabitants of a parish to contribute, whether by finance or labour. An Act of 1555 required that each parish should annually elect two parishioners as surveyors for one year and each year four (later six) days were set aside for road repairs when everyone was required to work for eight hours on each day or be fined. This system did not work well and the roads, especially between towns, generally fell into disrepair. Travel by coach was slow and could be dangerous. Jackman (*The Development of Transportation in Modern England*, Vol. II, 1916) records typical coach journeys in great detail. For example, London to Newcastle (290 miles) in 1754 was a six-day journey, London to Edinburgh (400 miles) took 10 days in summer and 12 days in winter, and Birmingham to London (110 miles) was two days in summer. Generally coaches in the mid-18th century seem to have averaged about 50 miles per day with average speeds of four to six miles per hour. The carriage of goods presented other problems. Although a certain amount was done by stage wagon, the majority was carried by pack horses, with long trains of animals making their way along the roads. This gave rise to the building of special bridges, the 'pack horse bridge', characterised by a narrow roadway about four feet in width with low parapet walls to allow the panniers to pass. Road maintenance was often of the most rudimentary kind, with gravel or earth thrown upon the highway to fill in potholes, and roads could become impassable, especially in winter.

In 1663 the first Act was passed to create a turnpike road between Wadesmill in Hertfordshire and Stilton in Huntingdonshire. Under the Act the Justices of the Peace were given powers to appoint nine 'sufficient and able' persons as surveyors of the highway. The Surveyors were, as before, empowered to require local people to repair and maintain the highway. In addition they were to appoint persons to collect tolls from those using the highway, to be spent on keeping the road in good repair.

From the early years of the 18th century, large numbers of turnpikes were created by Act of Parliament. Under a Turnpike Act groups of local trustees were given powers to levy tolls on the users of the turnpike road, usually a length of about 20 miles or less. In return for this power the trust was required to improve and maintain the road.

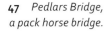

47 *Pedlars Bridge, a pack horse bridge.*

Gates were set up and tollhouses built to regulate traffic and collect the tolls. Scales of charges would be specified for different classes of traffic. Generally turnpikes were restricted to the main roads between towns, with local roads remaining a parish responsibility. The majority of the turnpike trusts were set up from about 1702 until the 1860s, with more than 1,300 trusts coming into being. Tolls were unpopular with travellers and in the early years bands of men would destroy gates and tollhouses. Wide-scale evasion of tolls was also rife even though penalties for non-payment were laid down in the Turnpike Acts. Turnpike Acts were for a limited period,

usually 21 years, following which the gates would be removed and no further tolls charged although the Act could be extended after the expiry of that period. Jackman (see above) records that there was much dishonesty as surveyors and toll collectors abused their offices for their own private ends. However, despite these difficulties the turnpike trusts generally succeeded in improving condition of the roads in their jurisdiction. There are many examples of turnpikes in the region. In 1840 in Shropshire there were over forty trusts including as an example the Bridgnorth Black Brook Trust, which controlled 7½ miles of road between Shrewsbury and Bridgnorth with one

main gate. Staffordshire had over fifty separate trusts, such as the Rugeley & Stone Trust with 27½ miles of road, five main gates and three side gates. Warwickshire, with 40 trusts, included the Stonebridge to Kenilworth Turnpike of 8.8 miles with three main gates.

Not all roads were covered by turnpike trusts, however, and often sections of turnpike would be separated by non-turnpiked sections. Over the c.150 years during which the turnpike trusts were active, about 16,000 miles of road came under the control of the trusts, but by the beginning of the 18th century it was realised that the turnpikes were not fulfilling their purpose, and from 1809 the Turnpike Acts were slowly revoked. Powers to maintain the roads were passed to the county through which the route passed, and county surveyors were appointed. Finance was provided from the county rate.

By the 1760s a new mode of transport was developing across the country – the canal (see Chapter 2). The canals provided a new method of transporting goods, more reliable and with less likelihood of damage than the pack horse or the stage wagon. Generally, much long-distance goods traffic was diverted onto the canal from the road; however, they did not offer a competitive alternative for passenger transport, which remained mainly road-based until the mid-1800s with the coming of the railways.

By the mid-1700s there was a need for a more scientific approach to road construction and maintenance. One of the first men to apply himself to this study was John Metcalfe who, although blinded by an attack of smallpox at the age of six, was able to undertake many road building contracts, mainly in Yorkshire and Lancashire but also in Derbyshire and Cheshire. 'Blind Jack of Knaresborough' (as he was known) was a pioneer but the most distinguished names connected with the development of the modern system of road construction are those of Thomas Telford and John Loudon McAdam. Indeed, the principles of road pavement construction using a layered structure were developed by these two and remain in use to this day, the main modern improvement being in the range and quality of the construction materials now available.

Telford and McAdam developed the science of road building independently by recognising that the road structure performed three

48 *(Opposite) Telford Toll House on the Holyhead Road.*

49 *(Opposite) Blind Jack Metcalfe of Knaresborough.*

50 *(Below left) John Loudon McAdam.*

51 *Thomas Telford.*

separate functions. Firstly, it must protect the underlying natural soil from the effects of rain and frost which severely weaken its carrying capacity. Secondly, the pavement must distribute the weight of the traffic using the road so that the underlying natural soil is not overloaded and so damaged. Thirdly it must provide a smooth running surface for the wheels of the passing traffic. Both men devised similar methods of construction and maintenance which satisfied these requirements. They realised that in order for the supporting soil to remain strong it needed ditches alongside the road to drain the soil under the road and carry away surface water. This was also assisted by raising the level of the road above the surrounding ground. On the dry foundation thus achieved the road was built up in a series of layers of broken stone, the maximum size of stone progressively decreasing towards the surface. At the top a smooth running surface was made up of small stones and gravel. With the passage of the iron-tyred vehicles of the time, the surface stones would be crushed and rolled, providing a waterproof surface which was cambered to allow any water to run off into the ditch. Although there were great similarities between the Telford and McAdam systems, generally McAdam's roads were less massive than Telford's and probably more economical.

McAdam was appointed surveyor to the Bristol turnpike trust in January 1816 and was able to put his new ideas into practice. Over the next 20 years he worked for more than twenty turnpike trusts until his death in November 1836. His name lives on in the terms 'macadamised road' and 'tarred macadam' (or 'tarmac').

Thomas Telford is remembered for his work on improving the road between London and Holyhead in the 1820s. In 1815 Telford was asked by the government to report on the state of the Holyhead Road, an important link in communication with Ireland. He reported in 1817 and following the setting up of the Holyhead Road Commission he was appointed its Engineer. Over the next nine years or so he and his assistants supervised the construction of new roads and the improvement of existing roads on the route. The route of Telford's road does not completely follow the present A5, leaving it at Weedon and rejoining it at Wellington, travelling via Coventry, Birmingham, Wolverhampton and Shifnal. A significant proportion of the route lies within the West Midlands region, from Coventry in the east to the Welsh border at Chirk. In Wales Telford designed and built a mainly new road, but in England he directed trusts to improve existing turnpikes. The improvements consisted mainly of reducing gradients and rebuilding the road to Telford's specifications. For example, at Meriden, west of Coventry, on the section of turnpike controlled by the Dunchurch & Stonebridge Trust, Telford's improvements can still be seen, with the old road on a gradient of 1 in 12 being replaced by a new alignment south of the old route and the gradient reduced to 1 in 20. Telford's new road, although widened for modern traffic, is still in use today. Telford made regular reports to the Commissioners detailing progress and the road was finally completed by the mid-1830s, after Telford's death.

Telford's construction method required the levelling and draining of the road foundation, with cross-drains every 100 yards along the road connected to ditches on either side. On the prepared foundation was laid a layer of large stones, placed by hand as close together as possible, with their broad ends downward. This layer was seven inches deep in the middle and five inches deep at the edge. The top stones were no wider than three inches. The interstices were packed with smaller stones. Then followed a further six inches of stones weighing not more than six ounces and passing through a 2½-inch ring. The final surfacing was a 1½-inch thickness of gravel which soon became a dense layer under the passage of wheels and horses hooves. A cross-camber of about four inches was provided on the 30ft-wide carriageway. Ever a thorough engineer, Telford designed not only all the elements of the new road including its tollhouses with characteristic overhanging eaves, the iron toll gates in a 'rising sun' pattern and the mileposts, but also the tools used in the works. Examples of a tollhouse, toll gate and milepost may be seen at the Blists Hill Museum at Ironbridge and several examples of the toll houses are still extant along the line of the road.

52 *Telford Tollgate from Holyhead Road, now at Blists Hill Museum.*

The work of Telford and McAdam greatly improved the quality of the road system but unfortunately, as mentioned above, their new developments coincided with the development of the railways and the roads lost much of their traffic to the new mode of transport with its greater speed and convenience. Consequently for the next 70 years or so the road network was often neglected. The road mender with his roadside hut and stock of broken stone was a familiar sight in those times. However, road transport was still an important aspect of travel for both passenger and freight in towns and cities and some developments in road construction took place in these areas. To provide a harder-wearing surface in comparison with the water-bound macadam surface developed by Telford and McAdam, stone paving was mainly used. This consisted of small stone blocks, or setts, laid on a granular bed, with the stones shaped to provide a grip for the hooves of horses. However, they were extremely noisy and as traffic increased ways of reducing this nuisance were sought. Wood block paving was tried from the 1830s onwards. Usually hardwood blocks were laid with the grain of the timber vertical and, with improvements in construction, roads lasting up to 20 years were achieved. Unfortunately both stone setts and wood blocks proved unsuitable for mechanically propelled vehicles due to the slippery nature of the surface, especially when wet, but block-paved urban streets did not completely disappear until after the Second World War.

The next development to revive interest in the road system was the coming of the mechanically propelled vehicle. Starting with steam-powered traction engines and subsequently steam lorries, the great upsurge in road traffic came with the development of the internal combustion engine by Gottlieb Daimler in Germany in the 1880s. Motor cars and lorries became a familiar sight on British roads from the turn of the 20th century. Initially the problems generated by the coming of the motor car were associated with the road surface. With its greater speed, the motor vehicle generated strong air currents which damaged the soft water-bound macadam road surface and early photographs of motor vehicles in motion usually show them accompanied by clouds of dust thrown up from the road surface. This generated loose stones and pot holes which, filling with water, rapidly led to a deterioration of the running surface. The development of the pneumatic tyre by John Boyd Dunlop in 1887 had made the situation worse as the soft tyres picked up and scattered the loose stones.

Fortunately, there were available two materials which, when mixed with the surface stones, were able to overcome these problems. The first of these was tar, derived from the extensive gas and coke industry, suitably refined, and the second was bitumen, the material remaining after the distillation of crude petroleum oil. Experiments in the use of tar as a binding agent for the road surface material had been made as early as about 1830 and asphalt had been used for surfacing streets in Paris in the 1850s, but there was no real impetus for their widespread use until the coming of the motor vehicle. By mixing a suitable proportion of the hot 'binder' (as it came to be known) with the stone, a material was produced which, upon cooling, had the stability to resist the wear of modern traffic and, as a bonus, providing a waterproof layer.

These new materials became known as 'coated macadams', with 'tarred macadam' or 'tarmac' becoming a popular name for all materials of this type. Since they were first widely introduced in the early years of the last century, the original tarred macadams, by varying the type and amount of the binder and the type and grading of the stone, have blossomed into a large family of related materials. Within this family are found today's high-strength bituminous materials, both macadams and asphalts, which significantly strengthen the pavement structure to resist the heavy and frequent loading applied to our roads by modern traffic.

One further construction material which has been adapted for road construction is concrete. Although there had been some use of concrete as one of the layers of the road pavement, the construction of wholly concrete road pavements did not develop significantly in the UK until about 1920, when some experimental pavements were constructed. These early trials led to the widespread use of concrete pavements. In the inter-war years many miles of bypasses were constructed in concrete, often including experimental sections designed to assist in developing a correct specification for concrete pavement construction. One of its weaknesses has been the need to provide

53 *A38(M) Aston Expressway showing tidal flow in operation.*

49

joints in the pavement structure to allow for shrinkage and temperature-induced expansion and contraction of the material but developments since the 1980s had begun to eliminate this problem. Concrete surfaces also need to be roughened for adequate skid resistance. However, the construction of wholly concrete roads has now largely ceased due mainly to the problem of noise generated by vehicles running over the roughened road surface.

During the 20th century rapid progress was made in creating a modern road network to accommodate the rise of the mechanically propelled vehicle. In 1909 a tax was imposed on fuel in order to provide finance for the improvement and building of roads. This finance was administered by the Road Board. In 1913 a system of classifying roads was started which divided roads into three classes, the first two of which would receive government grants towards the cost of maintenance. In 1919 the Road Board was abolished and the Ministry of Transport was created. In 1946 the first plan for a national network of motorways was published but post-war economic circumstances delayed the building of the first motorway, the Preston Bypass (now a section of the M6) until 1958. Subsequently a large network of over two thousand miles has been developed and it is interesting to note that, as with the railways, the West Midlands was the target of the first long-distance route to be completed, the M1 London to Birmingham motorway. Today the West Midlands is an important focus of motorway development with the M6, M5, M40, M42 and M54 all crossing the area. In Birmingham on the M6 is one of the most complex motorway interchanges in Britain, the **Gravelly Hill Interchange (WM6)**, which links the M6 with the A38(M) Aston Expressway and local roads including the A38 Lichfield Road. The Aston Expressway is one of the few national roads to feature 'tidal' flow, with its seven lanes allowing four to be used inbound towards Birmingham in the morning peak hour and four lanes outbound in the evening peak.

Thus the road, the earliest form of transport, has regained in the 20th and 21st centuries its position as the pre-eminent transport mode for both passenger and freight.

U p until the middle of the 18th century, one of the major causes of disease and suffering among the population was a lack of a safe water supply. All too often sources from wells and rivers, especially in the growing towns and cities, were contaminated. This was frequently due to pollution from untreated sewage which was usually discharged into the nearest water course. Starting with the passing of the first Public Health Act in 1848, efforts began to be made to tackle this problem by providing clean water supplies and safe drainage. This chapter considers the contribution of the civil engineer towards the provision of safe water supplies, drainage of waste water and sewage treatment and the provision of power to industry through the construction of wind and water mills and, more recently, the development of domestic and industrial gas and electricity supply systems.

WATER SUPPLY

The provision of clean water has been an important factor in the general health of the population from ancient times. The Romans were among the first to develop water supply systems, often bringing water to their towns from great distances. Some of their finest structures were aqueducts and many of these are still to be found worldwide, a good example being the Pont du Gard Aqueduct in southern France. However, in Britain, following the end of the Roman occupation water supply systems fell into disrepair and most water was obtained from local wells which often became contaminated. Following the four great epidemics of cholera in the 19th century, the discovery that it was a water-borne disease prompted improvements in water treatment and supply systems, particularly in London and other large towns. Local water companies were set up to use local sources, construct treatment works and distribution systems and charge tariffs for the supply of water to homes and factories. A significant piece of legislation was the 1875 Public Health Act which created local health boards with power to ensure proper water supply.

Water is supplied from three primary sources, from underground supplies from springs or by pumping from wells or from surface water from rivers and streams. Water must be stored to accommodate the fluctuating supply and demand. On a large scale these take the form of open storage reservoirs, often of great capacity and situated where they may be most readily supplied with water. Rainfall-fed reservoirs are most frequently found in areas of high rainfall, notably upland areas from which the water is conveyed by pipeline to the supply area. A notable local example is the Elan Valley water supply scheme. In 1890 James Mansergh was asked to look into the improvement of the water supply to Birmingham and he recommended that a number of new storage reservoirs be built in the Elan Valley near Rhayader in central Wales with a pipeline, the Elan Valley Aqueduct, to carry the stored water the 73½ miles to Birmingham. The water is driven by gravity, the aqueduct intake being 167ft higher than the top water level at Frankley Reservoir in Birmingham. The aqueduct has about 36½ miles of conduit in which the water flows at atmospheric pressure and 37 miles of pipeline within which the water flows under pressure. The scheme was designed for an ultimate flow of 75 million gallons per day (mgd) and the first water was supplied in July 1904. By contrast, the main water supply to the city of Coventry is obtained from the River Avon at Strensham, near Tewkesbury, from where, after treatment, it is pumped to local covered storage reservoirs at Meriden. At a local level the covered service reservoir is essential to balance supply during daily fluctuations in demand and in dry periods. They may be of considerable size, the Meriden reservoirs referred to above having a combined capacity of 35 million gallons.

54 *Pont du Gard Roman Aqueduct, France.*

55 *Elan Valley water supply scheme: Craig Goch dam and reservoir.*

A local water supply system with a particularly long history is the one serving the City of Lichfield. As with many of the early local supply systems it has monastic origins. Between about 1140 and 1170 there are records of payments made by the canons of Lichfield Cathedral for the supply of water from springs at Pipe, near Burntwood. The water was piped over a distance of 1½ miles to the Cathedral Close. Water was being piped into the houses of the canons by 1300 and in 1301 permission was granted to the friars of Lichfield Friary to pipe water from springs about half a mile away to the friary. The town also had a water supply from the Middle Ages after an aqueduct was provided in the 1270s. The friary's supply was also extended into the town by 1482. Following the dissolution of the friary its supply passed into private hands but in 1550 was granted to the corporation at an annual rental of four pence. In 1545 lands were granted to a trust, the income from which was to be used to maintain the town's water supply, and this trust continued to supply water until the 20th century. Over the next 200 years the town supply was gradually extended and private connections to houses were made. Reservoirs were built and the old wooden and lead pipes were progressively replaced by iron. In 1876 the original supply to the Cathedral Close was connected to the town supply, remaining in partial use until 1969 when it was abandoned. In the 19th century population growth required the improvement of the supply system and the establishment of new sources of water. In 1855 the South Staffordshire Waterworks Company (SSWC) was established to supply water to the outlying parts of the city from a pumping station at Sandfields. Although the networks of the trust and the SSWC were physically linked in 1923 it was not until 1930 that the whole city was supplied by the waterworks company. Private and public wells were also in use in the town but as the piped supply was extended the use of these wells was gradually discontinued until by 1959 only three properties in the city were without a piped supply.

Raw water from surface or underground supplies must be treated before it can be supplied to the customer. Water treatment normally consists of chemically purifying the water and coagulating the solid particles, followed by filtration to remove suspended solids. A small amount of chlorine is then added to disinfect the supply before it is piped to local covered service reservoirs and thence to the customer. Water treatment works are not normally accessible although open days may be held on occasions, but open storage reservoirs are often accessible to the public and play a major role in the provision of leisure facilities. Water distribution systems normally use underground supply pipes but a more visible feature of the local supply system is the water tower. These tall structures, topped with a tank, provide storage to accommodate local fluctuations in demand during the day and, especially in flatter areas, provide an elevated supply to guarantee adequate pressure in the local supply network. Most water towers are provided for supply to the local population but may also be provided for particular sites, a hospital or military depôt for example. Originally built of brick or stone, more modern examples are usually of concrete or steel. A particular example of the all-steel water tower is the Braithwaite type in which the tank is formed from standard prefabricated pressed steel panels, bolted together to produce a tank of the required dimensions. The tank is supported on a lattice steel structure as at Corley near Nuneaton. Sometimes other structures have been adapted for use as water towers; **Tainters Hill Tower (WK18)**, an example in Kenilworth, Warwickshire, is an old windmill adapted by constructing a water tank on top of the mill tower. This

56 *Braithwaite-type water tower at Corley near Nuneaton.*

tower, as with others, has been subsequently converted into a house. Other examples of water towers in the region will be found in the Gazetteer.

Another visible manifestation of the water supply system is the pumping station, either to extract water from a well or borehole or to provide the means of conveying the water from the catchment to the supply area. Although modern pumping stations are usually electrically powered, there are some fine examples of Victorian pumping stations preserved along with the steam engines that powered their pumps. These are often imposing buildings with an ornate visual appearance, reflecting their importance to the local community and the water company

57 *Whitacre Pumping Station.*

which built them. The illustration shows the ornate buildings of Whitacre Pumping Station near Birmingham rising like a Rhine castle above the trees, although this particular building lost its steam engines in the 1950s. Of particular note in the region are the pumping stations at **The Bratch (ST32)** and **Milmeece (ST22)** in Staffordshire, which have retained their steam engine plant and are described in the Gazetteer section of this volume.

DRAINAGE AND SEWAGE TREATMENT

Although where possible, drainage systems utilise gravity to enable the flow of waste water to the treatment works, it is sometimes necessary to provide a pumping station. A fine example is at **Claymills (ST2)**, a Victorian steam-powered pumping station just to the east of Burton upon Trent which was built in 1885 to pump the sewage from the town through an outfall sewer to a sewage farm situated 2½ miles away. The two large engine houses each contain two Woolf compound beam engines, which both drove

58 *Claymills sewage pumping station, Burton upon Trent.*

two ram pumps. Designed by James Mansergh, the engines and pumps were designed to deliver 5.5 million gallons per day through twin 27in-diameter cast-iron pipelines. Two of the engines have recently been restored to working order. As with water supply systems (above), modern pumping of waste water is normally electrically powered.

Before the treatment of waste water can begin it is necessary to provide a drainage system to convey it to the purification works. Waste water drainage systems comprise networks of underground pipes, occasionally of large size, which are normally laid under streets with connections from houses and factories. Domestic waste water normally poses no particular problems but some types of trade waste require special treatment at the factory before being discharged to the main sewer system. Little evidence of the drainage system exists at ground level other than the familiar manhole cover which allows access to the sewers for cleansing and maintenance. In more modern networks two pipes are usually provided, one for contaminated waste water and one for the rain water which drains from roofs, roads and other paved surfaces. This surface water is normally discharged locally to a convenient water course and requires no treatment. In many of the older parts of towns and cities only a single pipe was provided to convey both types of water. Many of these are still in use today, causing difficulties in times of high rainfall if they become overloaded. The contaminated water is conveyed to the treatment works where the process of purification begins.

In the early days of waste water treatment the treatment process was very simple. Large sewage farms were created where the waste water was spread over fields and left to dry before the land was ploughed and used for crops. In more recent times the treatment of waste water normally comprises four major stages. Firstly, large solids are removed from the incoming flow by screens; then the sewage is held in large tanks to settle out the smaller organic solids as sludge. Next, the settled sewage is exposed to air in order to encourage aerobic bacteria to purify the contaminated water. There are several different methods by which this exposure may be achieved, one being the rotating sprinkler, more commonly found on smaller treatment works, or aeration in special tanks where air is introduced into the sewage by agitating the flow with paddles or underwater air diffusers. This treatment also has the effect of producing more settleable solids which are removed before the treated water is discharged to a nearby watercourse. The sludge produced at the two settlement stages of the process is usually treated in modern works by 'digestion' in heated closed tanks and dried, after which it may be used as a low-grade fertiliser. A by-product of the digestion process is renewable energy in the form of methane gas which can fuel the large engines powering electrical generators.

The second largest waste water treatment works in Britain and the largest waste water treatment works in the West Midlands region is at Minworth (SP 165922), near Coleshill, which treats much of the waste water from the Birmingham area. In 1870 the Minworth works was a sewage farm but in the 1930s the land could not cope with the rising use of water, and the works moved away from land irrigation to physical treatment. Over the intervening years the works has expanded not only due to population rise as a consequence of the rapid industrialisation of the area, but also since many smaller local treatment works have been closed and their flows diverted by way of a main trunk sewer to Minworth. The works now treats the sewage, including domestic and industrial sources, from a population of 1.7 million. An average of 110 million gallons of raw sewage are delivered to the works each day, which are treated by initial settlement followed by aeration in 24 large tanks where air is bubbled through the effluent. A final process of settlement takes place before the purified final effluent is discharged to the River Tame.

WIND AND WATER POWER

From earliest times wind and water have provided a source of power for local industry. The windmills and water mills were a familiar sight and several have survived to be restored in modern times. Both wind and water mills were used to power machinery, most frequently millstones, used for grinding processes such as the production of flour from grain or crushing flints for use in the potteries industry. Other mill-wheel powered processes included the crushing of mineral ores prior to refining, the 'fulling' of woollen cloth and water pumping for water supply or land drainage purposes.

A feature of the water mill is the mill pond, formed by damming the river. This provided not only a head of water to power the mill wheel but also a reserve for use in time of low river flow. Wheels could be undershot, where the water was fed at the bottom of the wheel; breast shot, where the water entered the wheel at half-height; or overshot, when the water flowed over the top of the wheel. The wheels were often large; for example each of the two low breast-shot water wheels at the flint-grinding **Chedddleton Mill (ST6)** are over twenty feet in diameter and over five feet wide. The wheel shaft drives a large vertical gear wheel (the pit wheel) inside the building which in turn drives a horizontal bevel gear (the wallower); its axle drives the mill machinery. Examples of water mills which can be visited are **Charlecote Mill (WK13)** (Hampton Lucy) and **Wellesbourne (WK42)** in Warwickshire, **Sarehole Mill (WM11)** in Birmingham and at **Cheddleton (ST6)** in Staffordshire.

Windmills are normally of one of three major types. The earliest type is the post mill. In this type of mill the whole of the upper part of the mill, including the sails and all the mill machinery, is housed in a timber building which rotates on a large timber post. The sails are brought into the wind by a long tail pole which is either manually powered or driven by a fantail at ground level. Secondly is the smock mill, similar to a tower mill but with a timber tower resting on a brick base. The tower is usually octagonal in shape and on top of the tower is a cap which rotates to bring the sails into the wind. Finally, the tower mill has a circular brick tower, on top of which is the timber 'cap' housing the sails, usually four but up to six. The cap rotates in order to bring the sails into the wind and is usually powered by a fantail with a small windmill operating a pinion to rotate the cap.

59   *Napton on the Hill Tower windmill.*

In all cases the sails drive an inclined shaft which, as in the case of water mills above, drives a large gear wheel (the brake wheel) meshing with a wallower gear to power a vertical shaft driving the mill wheels and other machinery. The sails are of two types. The older type is the common sail which is a framework of timber upon which is spread a canvas cloth. By adjusting the area of sail covered by the cloth the miller could control the power extracted from the wind. Later the patent sail was developed, which has spring-loaded slats that open when wind pressure is excessive and allow air to pass through the sail, thus preventing damage.

Often all that remains of the mill is the tower, shorn of its cap and sails, some of which have been converted into homes. However, there are several examples of windmills which have survived to be restored to working order, details of which will be found in the Gazetteer. Notable examples include **Chesterton Windmill (WK3)** in Warwickshire, built in 1632, with its unique arcaded tower; **Danzey Green post mill**

60 *Retort House of Birmingham's first gasworks in Gas Street.*

(WR4), now removed into preservation at the Avoncroft Museum of Buildings at Bromsgrove; and **Berkswell (WM1)** Windmill near Coventry.

Both wind and water mills were the work of the millwrights, skilled workers in wood, some of whom developed their skills to become early civil engineers. The most notable was James Brindley, who became a well-known canal engineer and whose exploits are covered in more detail in Chapter 2.

THE GAS INDUSTRY

The role of the civil engineer in the gas industry can be found mainly in the infrastructure for its transmission, distribution and storage. In conjunction with the other engineering disciplines, mechanical, chemical and gas, the design and construction of these facilities would have involved many early civil engineers to support the main production facilities.

The production of gas as a by-product from coal distillation to produce coke was known as early as the 16th century, but it was not until the beginning of the 19th century that its commercial manufacture and use became practicable. William Murdock, a Scot working as a site engineer in charge of Boulton & Watt's steam engines in Cornwall, first used coal gas for lighting in his house in Redruth in 1792 and by 1798 had invented the equipment to store the gas. Experiments in the use of gas for lighting were also being carried out in France, and Gregory Watt, son of James, knew of these and backed Murdock's work. Commercial gas plants for large mills were produced by Boulton & Watt from 1804, the first being installed by Murdock's pupil, Samuel Clegg, for lighting a cotton mill at Sowerby Bridge near Halifax in 1805, followed by Murdock's installation in a cotton mill in Manchester in 1806, and by 1814 over 30 small mill gasworks had come into existence.

By this time coal gas had been used to light streets in Westminster, supplied from the first city gasworks built in 1812/13. This had developed from independent demonstrations of gas lighting by Frederick Winsor in London in 1805-7, with an alternative system of supplying gas from a central gas production plant. By 1830 almost every city and large town in the country had a gasworks mainly built by private enterprise. The West Midlands was the site of two of the earliest gasworks in the world. Appropriately named Gas Street, adjacent to the canal basin of that name, was the site of Birmingham's first gasworks. The first works was built in 1818 and the retort house, which still exists although converted to other uses, dates from 1822. Gas production on the site ended in 1850 although the gas holders continued in use until the 1870s. At Saltisford in Warwick there remain the original buildings of **Warwick Gasworks (WK40)**, the town's first gasworks dating from 1822. Coal was delivered to the works from the nearby Saltisford canal basin, superseded by a tramway from the adjacent railway line after this opened in 1852. A more detailed description of the works will be found in the Gazetteer. The development of town gas systems required the construction of gas holders and gas distribution systems to store the gas and maintain pressure. The telescopic gas holder was developed in 1824.

Following the invention of the Bunsen burner in 1855, gas began to be used for cooking and heating as a significant improvement on coal. The first practicable gas fires followed over the next 20 years. In the towns, as well as street lighting, most public buildings and large stores had a supply, but it was not until the late 19th century that most homes had a gas supply following the introduction of the pre-paid gas meter.

Winsor's original gas company, the Gas Light and Coke Company continued until the gas industry was nationalised in 1949. The industry was privatised again in 1986. In 1994 the privatised British Gas split into two companies, with one dedicated to the transmission of gas via a national network.

Following the introduction of natural gas supplies, nearly all local municipal gasworks were closed and demolished; consequently little now remains of this large industry. The production of coke primarily for use in the metallurgical industry is still maintained. Natural gas can be found associated with oil or as an independent resource; it can also be manufactured from oil products. The first shipment of liquefied natural gas from Algeria arrived in Britain in 1964 but in 1965 gas was discovered in the North Sea and in between 1968 and 1976 Britain changed from the use of coal-derived town gas to natural gas with major construction work for storing and distributing gas from the gas fields in the North Sea taking place around the country. Over 275,000km of pipelines and gas mains now exist, with compressor stations to maintain pressure and new liquid and underground storage facilities for the gas.

Additional installations to enable the further import of liquefied natural gas by sea and new connecting pipelines bringing gas from Europe are recent additions as North Sea gas supplies are depleted.

THE ELECTRICITY INDUSTRY

Originally electrical power was generated from coal in the traditional power station together with a small amount of generation by hydro-electric stations. More recently gas-fired and nuclear-powered stations have been developed and wind and wave power is the latest power source to be exploited. The West Midlands was formerly the location of many coal-fired stations and just south of Worcester is the site of the region's only water-powered generating station and one of the first in the world. Powick Mills power station (SP 835524) was opened in 1894 and was powered by the waters of the River Teme on the site of an earlier water mill. The power station buildings remain but have now been converted for residential use. In Coventry, traces remain of the city's first power station (SP 333801), opened in about 1893 alongside Coventry Canal, from which it was supplied with coal. Adjacent to the power station site is a red brick building which is said to have been the power house for the Daimler motor car works that originally stood on the site. Most of the region's coal-fired power stations have now been closed and demolished and the sites redeveloped. Two of the few remaining generating stations still in use are Ironbridge Power Station (SJ 655038) with its four distinctive cooling towers and Rugeley B power station (SK 057179) in Staffordshire.

61 *Powick Bridge power station*

This section of the book is a descriptive list of civil engineering works, not only many of those referred to in previous chapters but many other sites which further illustrate the contribution of the civil engineer to mankind's progress over the last four centuries.

The sites are arranged by county and location, and a county map shows the approximate position of each site. For each site the following information is given:

- The location (name of town or village) with street name etc. where necessary.
- The national grid reference
- A brief description of the work
- If necessary the accessibility of the site and any access charges if appropriate.

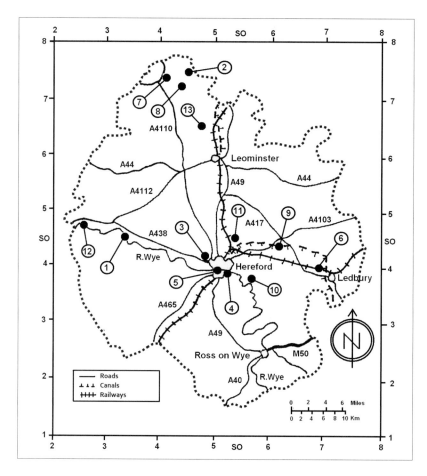

Map of Herefordshire (HE).

HE 1.   Bredwardine Bridge
HE 2.   Bringewood Forge Bridge, Downton
HE 3.   Herefordshire Water Works Museum
HE 4.   Victoria Bridge, Hereford
HE 5.   Wye Bridge, Hereford
HE 6.   New Mills Viaduct, Ledbury
HE 7.   Leintwardine Bridge
HE 8.   Burrington Bridge
HE 9.   Monkhide Bridge
HE10.   Mordiford Bridge
HE11.   Wergins Bridge, Sutton St Nicholas
HE12.   Whitney Toll Bridge
HE13.   Yarpole Bell Tower

BREDWARDINE

HE1. Bredwardine Bridge (SO 337447) has been rightly described as one of the finest brick bridges in England and is a six-span, red brick bridge carrying the road over the River Wye from Bredwardine to Staunton on Wye. It was built towards the end of the 18th century, having been authorised under an Act passed in 1762. The bridge had to be partially rebuilt following a flood in 1795. There are four spans over the river and one on each side over the river bank. The semi-circular arches each span about 32ft. The bridge stands level with the high bank of the river on the north side, but on the south side descends steeply to the lower south bank. There are cutwaters on both sides of the bridge which are extended up to roadway level to form pedestrian refuges, necessary as the roadway is only 13ft wide. It replaced a nearby ford and ferry. The bridge as it stands today was restored in 1922. It is readily accessible and is best viewed from the river bank on the south side of the river. (HEW 866)

DOWNTON ON THE ROCK

HE2. Bringewood Forge Bridge (SO 454750) is an impressively sited single-span semi-circular masonry arch bridge associated with one of the designers of the Iron Bridge. It carries a private road over the River Teme and originally gave access to the extensive iron working industries situated in the Downton Gorge area in the late 18th and early 19th centuries. The design of the bridge is associated with Thomas Farnolls Pritchard, a local architect. The main arch is 50ft span and the high arch is accommodated by the deep gorge in which the river flows. On both sides of the main arch are two small arches allowing passage along the river banks. The stone bridge is nicely detailed, with a castellated parapet and castellated turrets at the abutments. To the

62 *Bringewood Forge Bridge on the River Teme.*

south is a further arch spanning the old mill race that leaves the river about 100 yards upstream from the bridge, passing the site of the old water wheel buildings before going under the bridge and rejoining the river about 50 yards downstream. The race originally continued further downstream to the site of a former tin-plate works. Under the bridge is a fine semi-circular weir. The bridge was built in 1772 at the same time as Downton Castle (about a thousand yards west of the bridge) to replace an earlier timber bridge situated about 150 yards upstream of the present bridge. The bridge stands on private land but may be viewed from the public footpath that runs from the nearby minor road to the north and along the river bank to the east. (HEW 1278)

HEREFORD

HE3. Herefordshire Waterworks Museum (SO 497394) houses waterworks equipment in the old buildings of Hereford's first waterworks, the Lower Pumping Station of Hereford Waterworks. The function of the pumping station was to lift water from sumps fed by the River Wye through a vertical height of 100ft to the treatment works on Broomy Hill. The earliest buildings date from 1856 with subsequent additional buildings being developed over the next 50 years. Most of the original pumping equipment has been replaced but some of the later equipment is still in place. The original pumps were powered by two Simpson beam pumping engines. Later, due to increasing demand for water in the expanding town and the need to increase the supply pressure, a 100ft-high water tower was built on Broomy Hill and a further horizontal steam pump was installed at the Lower Pumping Station to supply the new tank. In 1895 a further bay was added to the building to house a triple expansion pumping engine and finally a further two-cylinder vertical pumping engine was installed in a final extension of the buildings in 1906. The pumping station has been superseded by the nearby modern Broomy Hill waterworks and now houses an interesting and extensive collection of waterworks artefacts, both from the pumping station and elsewhere. The museum's opening hours can be found on www.waterworksmuseum.org.uk. There is an admission charge. (HEW 1477)

HE4. Victoria Bridge (SO 512394) Victoria Bridge, one of the few suspension bridges in the region, is a footbridge crossing the River Wye about 400 yards downstream from the Wye Bridge. It was opened in September 1898 to commemorate the Diamond Jubilee of Queen Victoria of the previous year, replacing a ferry that had been in operation since 1893. It is a steel suspension bridge with a main span of 109ft 6in and two side spans of 37ft 6in. The suspension chains are made up from twin steel plates with vertical deck hangers from the joints in the chains. Each link of the suspension chain is 10ft 8in long. The lattice steel piers are pin-jointed at the base. The bridge was extensively repaired in 1967 but in August 2002 significant corrosion was found and the decision was taken to carry out major works on the bridge. These works include grit-blasting the steel to remove rust and old paint, repairing the steelwork and strengthening the bridge, renewing the timber deck and repainting it in its original cream colour.

63 *Victoria Bridge, Hereford.*

HE5. Wye Bridge (SO 508396) Situated in the centre of Hereford, this bridge is the oldest bridge over the River Wye. It has six spans and is still substantially as laid out in the 15th century albeit with considerable alterations in the 17th and 19th centuries. From the north end of the bridge the arches numbered 1, 2, 4 and 5 are late 15th-century four-centred arches. The old arches are set back and those in spans 4 and 5 are partly obscured by widening carried out in 1826. Arch number 3 was demolished in 1645 and rebuilt after the Civil War in a segmental form with three shallow ribs. The southernmost arch, number 6, has a plain 17th-century or earlier arch supported by an 18th-century arch. Further arches of a higher profile were added to both sides of the bridge in 1826 to enable widening of about three feet to take place on either side. The parapet was also rebuilt at this time and has subsequently been extensively repaired. This bridge, which is listed Grade 1, is an important example of medieval bridge building. It can be viewed from the river bank on the south side of the river. (HEW 1879)

64 *Wye Bridge, Hereford.*

LEDBURY

HE6. New Mills Viaduct (SO 702388) A relatively large 31-arch brick viaduct dating from 1860 carries the Worcester to Hereford railway line across a small stream and the River Leadon west of Ledbury. The viaduct, which carries the railway 75ft above the river, is on a slight curve. The semi-circular arches have a span of 30ft and are supported on brick piers about 5ft thick. The structure is basically plain with a single string course of rounded brick above the arch ring. The designer of the viaduct was Charles Liddell and the contractors were Thomas Brassey with his partner Stephen Ballard, whose first experience of civil engineering had been on the Herefordshire & Gloucestershire Canal (see Monkhide below). It is possible to view the viaduct from the nearby A438 road. (HEW 1987)

65   *New Mills Viaduct, Ledbury.*

66   *Leintwardine Bridge.*

LEINTWARDINE

HE7. Leintwardine Bridge (SO 404738) This five-span masonry arch bridge carrying the A4113 road over the River Teme is a representative example of a bridge by John Gethin, an important local bridge builder (see below). It is sited probably on or near the Roman road crossing of the river just south of the Roman fort of *Branogenium*. The alignment is north-south with four river piers. The arches are segmental and the spans vary from 21ft 7in to 15ft 4in and the total length of the bridge is about 110ft between the abutments. The bridge was built in 1779-80 by John Gethin senior and originally was only 12ft wide. In 1931 it was widened to the present width of 24ft. The drawings for the widening show that the original voussoir face stones were re-used on the new west face of the bridge and new arch stones were obtained from Longton, Thinghill and the Sutton Aqueduct. The bridge can best be viewed from the bank on the north-east side. (HEW 1906)

HE8. Burrington Bridge (SO 436721) is one of three larger bridges built in Herefordshire by John Gethin. It carries an unclassified road over the River Teme south-east of Leintwardine and was completed in 1813. The single masonry segmental arch spans 54ft. The bridge has a decorated horizontal string course above the arch, and the arch and spandrels are recessed, a characteristic of Gethin's bridges. He was born on 30 November 1757 and was trained as a stonemason, following his father's trade. He began working on bridge repairs for the Herefordshire Quarter Sessions, then responsible for bridge maintenance, in the 1790s and in October 1799 was appointed Surveyor of the County Bridges, the first holder of that office in Herefordshire. Over the next few years Gethin produced plans and estimates for bridge construction and repair, frequently carrying out the work himself as contractor if no other offers were forthcoming. Between 1799 and 1831 he was responsible for the building of more than sixty bridges in the county, almost all single- or three-span structures. He continued in his position as County Surveyor until his death on 14 May 1831. Some other examples of Gethin's bridges are Pont ar Ynys (SO 327287), and Aymestry (SO 425655). A complete list of John Gethin's bridges can be found in *John Gethin, County Surveyor* by P.S.M. Cross-Rudkin, and P.T. Shaw in *Transactions of the Woolhope Naturalists Field Club 2001*. (HEW 1979)

MONKHIDE
HE9. Monkhide Canal Bridge (SO 611440) An impressive example of skew arch bridge building. In 1843 the Herefordshire & Gloucestershire Canal was being extended from Ledbury, where construction had stopped for lack of funds in 1798. At Monkhide, a small village north-east of Hereford, the canal passed under a lane leading to the village. Here the Engineer, Stephen Ballard, designed a brick arch bridge with an extreme skew span. The square span of the bridge is only 18ft 6in but the skew span is about forty feet. Although the bridge is primarily brickwork, the outer edges of the arch are in finely dressed sandstone ashlar masonry. The brick parapets are capped with blue bricks stamped 'B.W. Blades, Maker, West Bromwich'. It might have been expected that a bridge of this nature would have been built at right angles to the canal and the road re-aligned to suit the bridge, with sharp bends on both sides. It is not certain why Ballard chose to build the bridge with such an extreme skew angle but it has been suggested that perhaps it was done as a private exercise in his skill and judgement. The bridge can easily be seen from the towpath of the canal, which is still in water in this section. The Herefordshire & Gloucestershire Canal Trust is actively pursuing the restoration of the canal at a number of sites along its length. (HEW 1874)

67 Aymestry Bridge shows the characteristic framing of the arch.

MORDIFORD
HE10. Mordiford Bridge (SO 569375) This bridge, south-east of Hereford, is reputed to be the oldest remaining bridge in Herefordshire. It is a complex structure with the main bridge having two arches over the River Lugg near its confluence with the River Wye. The river spans are in different styles, with one slightly pointed arch of 24ft span which has possibly existed since 1352, and the second arch with a span of 21ft, segmental in form, which probably dates from the 16th century. Both arches are ribbed, normally an indication of great antiquity. To the west of the river bridge there are several flood arches piercing the stone-walled approach road. Two of these arches are adjacent to the main bridge with three further flood arches to the west. The bridge has been widened and this can be seen on the western main arch, the original width of about 17ft defined by the three chamfered ribs. In the notes accompanying a recording of Edward Elgar's 'Elegy for Strings', composed in 1909, it is stated that at the end of his score is written 'Mordiford Bridge, 1909'. The bridge is visible from the roadway. (HEW 2083)

68 Monkhide Canal Bridge.

SUTTON ST NICHOLAS

HE11. Wergins Bridge (SO 529447) The bridge is notable in two respects. Firstly it is an early example of a reinforced concrete bridge; secondly it is a rare example of the use of the Kahn system. It is a single-span segmental arch bridge built in 1913 to replace an earlier bridge by John Gethin (see Burrington Bridge above). The Kahn system is a method of reinforced concrete construction in which the reinforcing bars are shaped with 'wings' which can be bent up to provide shear reinforcement rather than the use of separate shear reinforcement bars in more conventional types of reinforced concrete. The bridge spans 50ft over the River Lugg north-east of Hereford and is 26ft 6in wide. The arch is 38in thick at the abutments and tapers to 9in thick at the crown of the arch. The bridge has a masonry parapet with a plaque recording that the bridge was built in August 1913. A 60ft-long concrete wall downstream of the bridge and 5ft-wide mass concrete aprons at the base of the abutments are intended to protect the bridge foundations against the scour of the river bed. The designers were the Considère Construction Co. Ltd and the Trussed Concrete Steel Co. Ltd. The contractor was Andrew Scott of Port Talbot. (HEW 1960)

69 *Mordiford Bridge on the River Lugg.*

WHITNEY

HE12. Whitney Toll Bridge (SO 259474) A very rare combination of stone and timber in bridge construction. This unusual bridge carries the B4350 road to Hay-on-Wye across the River Wye west of the village of Whitney. In 1773 the owner of the then ferry, Mr Tomkyns Dew, lord of the manor of Whitney, presented a Bill in Parliament to author-ise a stone bridge at Whitney. Earlier bridges were destroyed by the river, the last being brought down by the great flood of February 1795 (many bridges on the River Severn were also damaged or destroyed by a great flood at this time). To replace this bridge, the hybrid stone and timber bridge we see today was proposed, but this type of construction required a further Act of Parliament which was passed in 1797. The present bridge has five spans; the central three spans are in timber with horizontal beams supported on timber piers. Each beam is supported by timber struts running at 45 degrees from the pier to the third point of the span. The two end spans are constructed in stone, the arch at the north end being semi-circular, the southern arch semi-elliptical. The piers are protected on the upstream side to prevent damage by floods and objects floating down the river. The bridge is one of a small number remaining which charge a toll for its use, most toll bridges (other than a small number of modern major bridges) having been bought out by highway authorities. (HEW 816)

70 *Wergins Bridge on the River Lugg.*

YARPOLE

HE13. Yarpole Bell Tower (SO 470649) Hereford-shire has four detached bell towers at Pembridge, Mamble, Knighton on Teme and Yarpole. Yarpole is the most complete and thought also to be the

71 *Whitney Toll Bridge on the River Wye.*

72 *Yarpole Bell Tower.*

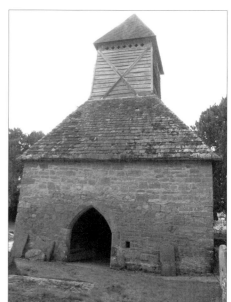

oldest. The tower, built to house the church bells, stands in the churchyard to the west of the church. The tower itself is formed from four massive oak posts framed together, each formed from a single slightly curved tree, squared into shape by axes. The timbers are 30ft long and 28in square at the base. The timbers have been dated by dendrochronology (tree-ring dating) to 1195 or 1196, the trees being about 200 years old when felled. There were several phases of construction. The original timber posts were extended by scarf-jointing further timbers with felling dates of 1322-66, which form the upper stage of the tower. These are framed together and would probably have supported a medieval bell frame. The horizontal boards with quatrefoil decoration at the top of the tower date from this phase. The final phase was the current bell frame at the top of the tower which carries three bells. The bells date from the 15th century, 1605 and 1652. The building is 26ft square with a stone wall about 2ft 6in thick. Above the walls is a sloping tiled roof, above which is the bell chamber with louvered sides. The tower is capped with a tiled roof. (HEW 2684)

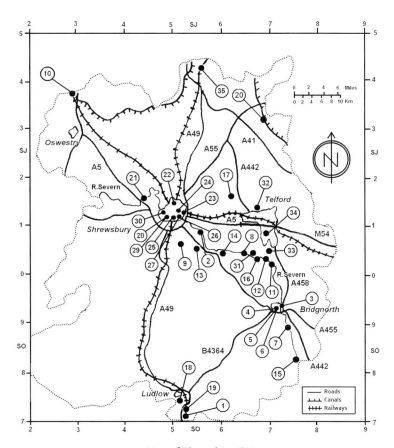

Map of Shropshire (SH).

SH 1. Ashford Carbonel Bridge
SH 2. Atcham Bridge
SH 3. Bridgnorth Bridge
SH 4. St Mary Magdalene Church, Bridgnorth
SH 5. Bridgnorth Cliff Railway
SH 6. Bridgnorth Railway Station
SH 7. Mor Brook Towpath Bridge
SH 8. Buildwas Bridge
SH 9. Cantlop Bridge
SH10. Chirk Aqueduct and Railway Viaduct
SH11. Coalport Bridge
SH12. The Hay Inclined Plane, Telford
SH13. Cound Arbour Bridge
SH14. Cressage Bridge
SH15. Borle Brook Towpath Bridge
SH16. The Iron Bridge
SH17. Longdon upon Tern Aqueduct
SH18. Ludford Bridge, Ludlow
SH19. River Teme Railway Bridge, Ludlow

SH20. Woodseaves Cutting, Market Drayton
SH21. Montford Bridge
SH22. Bage's Mill, Shrewsbury
SH23. Belvidere Railway Bridge, Shrewsbury
SH24. Castle Walk Footbridge, Shrewsbury
SH25. Coleham Pumping Station, Shrewsbury
SH26. The English Bridge, Shrewsbury
SH27. Greyfriars Bridge, Shrewsbury
SH28. Kingsland Bridge, Shrewsbury
SH29. Porthill Bridge, Shewsbury
SH30. Welsh Bridge. Shrewsbury
SH31. Albert Edward Bridge, Coalbrookdale
SH32. Hadley Park Locks, Telford
SH33. St Michael's Church, Madeley
SH34. St Leonard's Church, Malinslee
SH35. Whitchurch Station Footbridge

67

ASHFORD CARBONEL

SH1. Ashford Carbonel Bridge (So 520711) is a good example of a local bridge built under the supervision of Thomas Telford and remains largely unaltered. It lies on the road to Ashford Carbonel village from the A49 in the extreme south of the county and was designed by Thomas Stanton working for Thomas Telford. It was intended to be a brick bridge and William Atkins agreed to build it for £650 in a contract dated 4 June 1795. It fell during construction and Atkins forfeited his bond, but then agreed to build one of stone for an additional £150, to include his abortive work and the additional cost

73 *Ashford Carbonel Bridge.*

of the masonry. Telford, originally a stonemason himself, was closely involved in the selection of the stone to be used. A new specification was agreed on 18 January 1797, which stipulated that the bridge was to be open by 25 November that year. It has a single segmental masonry arch of 81ft clear span with a height of 24ft 6in above the springing of the arch. The arch ring, 27in thick, is mostly in gritstone but with some limestone blocks which have become etched by acid rain. The spandrel walls of the bridge are built in local red marlstone and it has a brick parapet. The roadway is about 16ft wide but as the bridge is situated on a minor road it has not been widened. It cost £830 to build, including the cost of the roadway, and a plaque on the bridge records that it was renovated and partially rebuilt in 1877. (HEW 1101)

ATCHAM

SH2. Atcham Bridge (SJ 541093), an elegant example of bridge building by John Gwynn and still in its original condition, is a seven-arch masonry bridge built between 1772 and 1779 that carried the Holyhead Road over the River Severn on the line of Watling Street at Atcham, east of Shrewsbury. Gwynn, a native of Shrewsbury, was a self-educated writer, architect and bridge builder. He was responsible for building two other bridges over the Severn, the English Bridge at Shrewsbury (see the entry under Shrewsbury) and Worcester Bridge, but Atcham Bridge is the only one which has not been altered during its life. Atcham Bridge is an exceptionally fine example of

74 *Atcham Bridge.*

an 18th-century masonry arch bridge. The first recorded bridge at Atcham was a 13th-century timber structure which was replaced some 300 years later by a stone bridge, built at the expense of Sir Rowland Hill. Gwynn's bridge was approved by the Quarter Sessions, which had responsibility for bridge building, in 1766. The original contract with Richard Buddle was for £5,000 but Buddle was released from the contract and the bridge was eventually completed by Gwynn at a total cost of £8,630. Built of local Grinshill stone, the spans vary in size from 32 to 43 feet. The bridge can be most conveniently viewed from the new bridge which runs parallel to it, which was built in 1927 using reinforced concrete with coloured cement and has a bush-hammered surface to

75 *Bridgnorth Bridge.*

match the old bridge, now restricted to pedestrian traffic. (HEW732)

BRIDGNORTH

SH3. Bridgnorth Bridge (SO 719930) at Bridgnorth is on the site of an ancient crossing of the River Severn which for some time was the only crossing between Atcham (see above) and Worcester. It has a long history. The first bridge, dating from about 1100, was probably of timber and this was replaced by a stone bridge known to have existed in the time of Edward II. It is possible that the westernmost, ribbed, arch of the present bridge may date from this time. The bridge has been much altered over its history, many of the repairs and alterations being made necessary by the frequent severe floods on the river, notably in 1741, 1770 and 1795. In 1802 Thomas Telford prepared a plan for rebuilding the two easternmost arches of the bridge, although the work was not carried out until about 1813. In 1823 the third and fourth arches from the west end were widened by John Smallman of Quatford. At the present time the bridge has six arches with a large pier between the fifth and sixth arches from the west end. In modern times the bridge was found to be inadequate for the volume of traffic using it and it was widened along its whole length using prestressed concrete beams supported on the cutwaters of the piers. The outer beams were clad in reconstructed stone to match the rest of the bridge. This work was completed in 1960. There is an excellent view of the bridge from the walkway near to the top station of the cliff railway (see below).

SH4. St Mary Magdalene Church (SO 717928) is a fine example of the early architectural work of Thomas Telford who, although best remembered for his work as a civil engineer, had in his early years been trained as a master stonemason. After coming to Shrewsbury in 1786 he was engaged to design several churches in the area. Probably the finest of these is St Mary Magdalene, the parish church of Bridgnorth. The church replaced an earlier building and due to the restricted nature of the site is, unusually, oriented north to south rather than the traditional east to west, facing down East Castle Street. The church was built between 1792 and 1795 by John Rhodes and Michael Head. Telford described the architecture of the church as 'outside is a regular Tuscan elevation; the inside is regularly Ionic; it is surmounted by a Doric tower'. The tower is 120ft high with a clock, eight bells and a copper-covered roof. Telford's aim with the interior of the church was to create a well-lit open space and it is simple in design with the almost

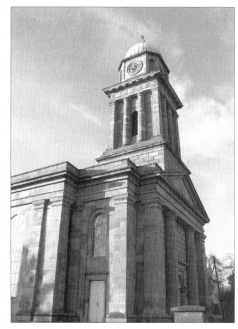

76 *St Mary Magdalene Church, Bridgnorth.*

77   *Bridgnorth Cliff Railway.*

78   *Bridgnorth station, Severn Valley Railway.*

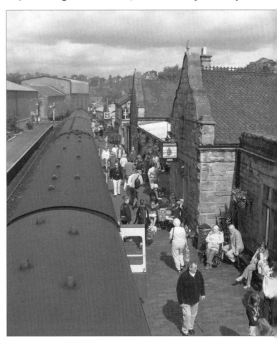

square nave being divided by two rows of columns with a gallery at the north end. There are large arched windows in plain glass, extending the full height of the side walls. The apse at the south end was added in 1876. The church presents its most striking view from East Castle Street. (HEW1134)

SH5. Bridgnorth Cliff Railway (SO 717930). Bridgnorth is the location of Britain's oldest inland cliff railway. It carries passengers from the Lower Town to the Upper Town, a vertical rise of 111ft. The railway has two cars running on two tracks and is cable hauled. The total length of the track is 201ft giving a gradient of 1 in 1.5 (66.7 per cent). The track gauge is 3ft 6in with flat-bottomed rails laid on sleepers bolted to the underlying rock. The twin cars each have a capacity of 18 persons. The railway was designed by G. Croydon Marks and built by G. Law. It opened on 7 July 1892. The cars were originally counterbalanced and connected by two steel cables supported on rollers in the centre of the track. A 2,000-gallon tank was provided under each car and the tank of the car at the upper station was filled with water from a 30,000-gallon reservoir. This provided sufficient out-of-balance weight for the upper car to descend and pull up the lower car. At the bottom of the railway the tank of the lower car was emptied and the water pumped back to the upper reservoir by two pumps powered by two gas engines. From 1944 the system was altered. Each car was provided with a separate haulage cable connected to one of a linked pair of haulage drums together with a common safety cable running over the original head wheel. Power is provided by a 32h.p. electric motor at the upper station. The cliff railway is still in operation today and provides a convenient alternative to the steep climb from the riverside to the Upper Town. (HEW 1703)

SH6. Bridgnorth Railway Station (SO 715926) is a typical station on one of Britain's major preserved steam railways and now forms one end of the line of the restored Severn Valley Railway. Originally opened in 1862, the station was on the line from Shrewsbury via Bewdley to Hartlebury. A short branch from Bewdley to Kidderminster provided an alternative route and it is this line which now forms part of the preserved

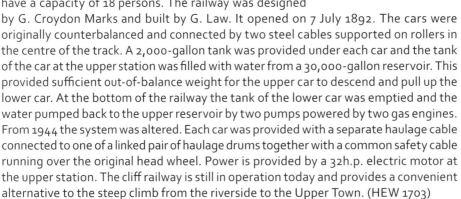

railway. The railway was built by contractors Brassey, Peto & Betts under its Engineer, John Fowler (later Sir John Fowler). The station at Bridgnorth has two platforms with stone station buildings on the east side. There is a lattice girder footbridge between the platforms. The station stands on high ground to the west of the town and was originally linked to it by a footbridge across the valley, but this was demolished and has now been replaced by the modern bridge seen today. The stations on the line were built by Eassie & Sons. On the west side of the station is the new engine shed and workshop erected by the Severn Valley Railway Company which undertook the restoration of the line, closed to through services in 1963, between Kidderminster and Bridgnorth. The restored line opened in stages, being opened between Bridgnorth and Bewdley in 1974 and extended to a new station at Kidderminster in 1984. (HEW 640)

SH7. Mor Brook Towpath Bridge (SO 733885). A few miles south of Bridgnorth the Mor Brook joins the River Severn from the west. In order to carry the towpath of the Severn across the mouth of the brook, John Onions of Broseley manufactured a cast-iron arch bridge which was erected in 1824. The single cast-iron segmental arch spans 30ft between its brick abutments. The arch and horizontal beam supporting the deck are cast in one piece. There is a low cast-iron parapet. The River Severn has always been an important artery of trade and until the early 19th century boats were hauled upstream by gangs of men. The coming of the canals with the resulting increase in river traffic fuelled a demand for a horse towing path which was built in stages until by 1812 there was a continuous horse path between Gloucester and Shrewsbury. The bridge can be reached by parking near the sharp bend in the B4555 road where it passes under the Severn Valley Railway, walking down alongside the Mor Brook to the Severn towpath where the bridge will be seen. There is a similar bridge at the confluence with the Borle Brook (see below). (HEW 972)

BUILDWAS

SH8. Buildwas Bridge (SJ 645045) has an interesting history, and is the fourth to stand on the site at the north end of the Ironbridge Gorge. The first was a medieval stone bridge which had just been repaired under Telford's supervision as County Surveyor when the disastrous flood of January 1795 swept it away. Telford was ordered to prepare plans and estimates for a new bridge, and he produced a plan for a single clear span cast-iron arch bridge to avoid placing piers in the river and thus allow for rapid changes in river level. The span was 130ft and breadth 18ft, the whole to be completed 'in a workmanlike manner' for the sum of £3,700. Telford's design was for a bridge with two superimposed arches. A lower, flatter, arch was designed to resist the inward pressure of the sides of the gorge, which are continually moving towards the river, together with a higher arch to carry the roadway. The Coalbrookdale Company also submitted a design for a new bridge but after arbitration by two ironmasters, John Wilkinson and William Reynolds, Telford's design was chosen. The contract was signed on 17 April 1795. The ironwork was cast by the Coalbrookdale Company and the bridge was completed on 24 June 1796. The final cost turned out to be nearer £6,000. Telford examined the bridge in 1818 and reported that repairs to the

79 *Mor Brook Towpath Bridge on the River Severn.*

wing walls and abutments were necessary. Unfortunately the tendency of the right bank to slip was never quite checked and in 1889 the main arch broke on the Ironbridge side due to the inward pressure. This was repaired by the Horsehay Company in 1890. In 1901 a further fracture occurred and Sir Benjamin Baker was called in. By then the condition of the arch was such as to warrant the recommendation of a new structure. The new bridge, the third on the site, was a steel lattice girder bridge of 130ft span with a deck width of 21ft 6in. It was anchored to the south abutment allowing freedom of movement on the north abutment, these being the original Telford abutments. When this bridge was built in 1905 these abutments had encroached three feet and by 1967 by a further three feet. This bridge in turn was demolished in 1992 and replaced by the modern concrete bridge seen today. (HEW 648)

CANTLOP

SH9. Cantlop Bridge (SJ 517063). Between 1811 and 1823 four similar cast-iron arch bridges were erected in Shropshire, all designed under the direction of Thomas Telford, then the Surveyor of Public Works for the county. Cantlop Bridge is the only one to survive in its original location. The other three were all dismantled and replaced, although one was rebuilt in a different location. Cantlop Bridge remains in its original position south of Shrewsbury on a minor road just north of Cantlop village. Built in 1812, the bridge has a single cast-iron arch of 32ft span. The four identical ribs of the arch are each cast in two halves, joined at the crown. There are iron deck plates supporting the roadway. In 1975 a new prestressed concrete bridge was built alongside the iron bridge, which was then preserved as an Ancient Monument. The other bridges referred to above were at Meole Brace, Shrewsbury (1811), dismantled in 1933; Cound (1818) on the Shrewsbury to Bridgnorth road, dismantled in 1969; and at Stokesay (1823), on the A49 Shrewsbury to Ludlow road, dismantled in 1969. It is believed that all these bridges were cast from a common mould, probably at Coalbrookdale, the length of

the mould being adjusted to accommodate the differing spans of the bridges. The ribs of Cound Bridge are now incorporated in a new pedestrian bridge at Telford town centre, spanning the B5072 road at grid reference SJ 695091. (HEW 330)

80 *Cantlop Bridge.*

CHIRK

SH10. Chirk Aqueduct and Railway Viaduct (SJ 287373). Chirk Aqueduct, which represents a development in aqueduct design by Thomas Telford and William Jessop, sits squarely on the border between England and Wales running along the line of the River Ceriog. The aqueduct carries the Ellesmere Canal (now known as the Llangollen Canal, part of the Shropshire Union system) 70ft above the river on 10 semi-circular masonry arches with a span of 40ft. The aqueduct is 710ft long. The contractor was Matthew Davidson. The foundation stone was laid on 11 June 1796 and it was completed in 1801. As seen today the canal is carried in a cast-iron trough supported by the masonry arches, but originally only the base of the trough was made up from cast-iron plates, flanged and bolted together. At the sides these plates were securely keyed into ashlar masonry and backed by brickwork set in Parker's cement. The iron trough sides were

81 *Chirk Aqueduct and Railway Viaduct.*

added about 1870. The adjacent 16-span railway viaduct was built in 1848. It was originally built for the Shrewsbury & Chester Railway, with the two outermost arches in laminated timber, the remainder being stone. The two timber arches were rebuilt in brick and stone in 1859. (HEW 111)

COALPORT

SH11. Coalport Bridge (SJ 702021) is one of the oldest cast-iron bridges in the county. The single arch has a span of 103ft and is 18ft wide. The date on the bridge parapet is given as 1818 but the present bridge was originally built in 1799. The construction of a toll bridge at the site was authorised by an Act of Parliament of 1777 (a year later than the Act for the Iron Bridge). This bridge consisted of two timber arches with a masonry pier at midstream; hence the name of the *Woodbridge Inn* on the south bank of the river.

82 *Coalport Bridge.*

Damage to the central pier from the great Severn flood of 1795 prompted the trustees to consider a single-span structure while the limited life of the timber arches together with the success of the Iron Bridge suggested the use of cast iron. It is believed that these proposals came to fruition in 1799 and the bridge then consisted of a single arch carried on three cast-iron ribs with a timber deck. Much of the present brickwork, founded on the earlier masonry, was erected during this reconstruction, which gave satisfactory service until 1817 when the centre arch rib of the three fractured. Tenders were invited for the reconstruction of the bridge in cast iron using the original arch ribs as far as possible and increasing the number of ribs to five. The tender of John Onions & Son was accepted and the work 'expeditiously carried out' in 1818, hence the date and initials on the parapet. The bridge, now subject to a severe weight restriction, was recently strengthened and renovated. A major engineering monument in its own right, Coalport Bridge is rather overshadowed by the precursor of all cast-iron bridges, the Iron Bridge, only a few miles upstream. (HEW 422)

SH12. The Hay Inclined Plane (SJ695028) This canal inclined plane is the only surviving example of a series of inclined planes in the East Shropshire canal system. It originally connected the Shropshire Canal with the River Severn at Coalport. The canal used tub boats 20ft long and 6ft 2in wide and these were raised and lowered in the dry, being transported on wheeled trolleys running on rail tracks. The plane has a vertical rise of 207ft in a length of approximately 300 yards, giving a gradient of about 1 in 4.3 (23 per cent). There were two parallel sets of rails, the two trolleys being linked by ropes to a common winding drum on which there was a brake wheel. As the main traffic was going downhill to the Severn, the heavier descending boat drew up the lighter ascending one. A steam engine at the upper level was used to lift the descending boat over the cill of the upper basin, thereafter it descended by gravity. In order to keep the tub boat approximately level, the upper axle of the trolley had smaller diameter wheels than the lower axle, and to keep it level as it went over the cill of the upper basin additional wheels on the outside of the upper axle engaged with side rails to lift the small wheels off the track. This was an ingenious device which seems to have been perfected by William Reynolds, then in control of the Coalbrookdale Company and its many local interests. The plane was under construction in 1792-3. The Hay plane was equivalent to a flight of 21 locks and was worked by only four men. It could pass a pair of tub boats in 3½ minutes whereas traditional locks would have taken many hours. Shortly after the Ironbridge Gorge Museum Trust was formed in 1968, the upper and lower basins and track of the incline, which had long been disused, were cleared and the rail tracks replaced. The plane can be viewed from the road at its foot and is now part of the Blists Hill Open Air Museum. (HEW 639)

83 *The Hay Inclined Plane, Blists Hill Museum.*

84 *Cound Arbour Bridge.*

85 *Cressage Bridge.*

COUND

SH13. Cound Arbour Bridge (SJ 555053), also known as Church Bridge and Lawns Bridge, is the oldest iron bridge in the county still carrying unrestricted traffic. It carries a minor road over the Cound Brook, just off the A458 road near the village of Cound. The bridge has three cast-iron arch ribs with a span of 36ft and was cast at Coalbrookdale and erected in 1797. The outer ribs have circles of diminishing size filling the spandrels; the inner rib is of a different design. It has been suggested that the bridge was designed by John Dodson but there is no written evidence for this. The iron deck plates were originally carried on filling materials but in 1931 the county council replaced this with concrete, which also invisibly strengthened the bridge. (HEW 423)

CRESSAGE

SH14. Cressage Bridge (SJ 594045) This is a reinforced concrete arch bridge of three spans of 40, 80 and 40ft and is a good example of the transition from masonry to reinforced concrete, the external design being strongly based on masonry practice. Immediately north of the village of Cressage, the B4380 road crosses the River Severn. A privately owned timber trestle toll bridge of five spans was built about 1800 to replace a previous bridge damaged in the great flood of 1795. This bridge was purchased by the county council in 1913 who removed the tolls, demolished the timber bridge and replaced it with the present structure. It is an early example of this type of construction and was designed by L.G. Mouchel. (HEW 1100)

HIGHLEY

SH15. Borle Brook Towpath Bridge (SO 753817). About one mile south of Highley the Borle Brook meets the River Severn. To carry the towpath of the river across the mouth of the brook a cast-iron arch bridge was erected in 1828. Cast by the Coalbrookdale Company the arch spans about 41ft and each of the two arch ribs is made up of two half-ribs with a bolted joint at the crown. The bridge is 5ft 6in wide inside the parapets. A feature of the bridge is the attractive diminishing roundels within each arch rib. The bridge can be reached by walking about one mile downstream along the river bank

86 *Borle Brook Towpath Bridge on the River Severn.*

87 *The Iron Bridge*

88 *Cast-iron trough of Longdon upon Tern Aqueduct, Shrewsbury Canal.*

from Highley Station on the Severn Valley Railway (see also Mor Brook Bridge above). (HEW 977)

IRONBRIDGE

SH16. The Iron Bridge (SJ 672033) is probably the best-known civil engineering work in the region and is the centre piece of the Ironbridge Gorge World Heritage Site. When it was opened on 1 January 1781 it was the first bridge in the world to be constructed wholly in iron. The bridge clears the river in a single span of 100ft 6in and carries the roadway 40ft above the normal river level. The arch is made up of 10 half ribs, each cast in one piece by Abraham Darby III at his Coalbrookdale furnace and jointed at the centre. It contains just over 378 tons of iron and survived the notorious Severn floods to carry vehicular traffic until 1931, when it was closed to all but pedestrians. The bridge is also notable for its style of construction. Nearly all the joints between the members of the bridge are in the form of mortise and tenon and dovetail joints, which would be much more familiar in a timber bridge. The patterns for the parts of the bridge were made by Thomas Gregory, foreman pattern maker at Coalbrookdale. One of the people involved in the design of the bridge was Thomas Farnolls Pritchard, a local architect who had been involved a few years earlier in the design of Bringewood Forge Bridge in Herefordshire (see above) to which the form of the Iron Bridge bears a resemblance. Until recently the method by which the bridge was erected across the river was not known except for a statement that the river was not obstructed during the erection. However, the emergence in 1997 of a watercolour sketch painted by a Swedish professor at the time of the building of the bridge shows the arches supported by a temporary scaffolding. This evidence gave rise to a possible erection sequence which was tested on a half-scale model of the bridge at Blists Hill Museum that showed the method was feasible. (HEW 136)

LONGDON UPON TERN

SH17. Longdon upon Tern Aqueduct (SJ 617156) carried the Shrewsbury Canal over the River Tern, a small tributary of the Severn. The site of the aqueduct is close to the Wellington to Shawbury road, B5063, about five miles north-west of Wellington.

89 *(Opposite, left) Ludford Bridge.*

90 *(Opposite, right) River Teme Railway Bridge near Ludlow.*

In 1793 Josiah Clowes was appointed as Engineer for the construction of the canal and commenced the building of a conventional masonry arch aqueduct at Longdon. However, Clowes died in December 1794 and Thomas Telford was appointed in his place. In 1795 the Longdon aqueduct was damaged by floods and Telford's design for the iron aqueduct was approved in March 1795.When it was completed in 1795 it was the first major cast-iron canal aqueduct in Britain although a small, less successful, cast-iron aqueduct was built on the Derby Canal at about the same time. The central section of the aqueduct is a cast-iron trough nine feet wide and three feet deep supported over a length of 186ft by three sets of cast-iron columns and raking struts. The towpath of the canal is carried over the aqueduct level with the base of the trough on cantilevered brackets. The trough is built up from individual plates which are bolted together. The two ends of the aqueduct are in brickwork; the small arches characteristic of the early Brindley type of aqueduct are almost certainly the remnants of Clowes' original aqueduct. It can be reached along a footpath running from the B5063 road just to the east of the aqueduct. (HEW 280)

LUDLOW

SH18. Ludford Bridge (SO 512742), a massive ancient bridge, has an interesting history of widening and modification. It is a three arch masonry structure on the old A49 trunk road which crosses the River Teme on the south side of Ludlow. The bridge dates from the 15th century and is the latest in a series of rebuilds on the same site since 1150. The ribbed segmental arches spring from massive piers with spans of 32ft 2in, 32ft 4in and 28ft 10in and the width between the parapets is 12ft. In 1866 a flood carried away most of the structure above the arches and the upper parts were rebuilt in a greyish sandstone which contrasts with the earlier, lower, parts in pink sandstone. The cutwaters of the piers are carried up to roadway level to provide pedestrian refuges. In the south-eastern corner of the bridge is a skew arch which has allowed the corner to be widened. This was added in the early 19th century at the request of the Post Office after problems with mail coaches making the turn off the bridge. In more modern times this technique has also been applied at the north-eastern corner of the bridge using a reinforced concrete slab cantilevered from an underlying reinforced concrete beam. The bridge can be viewed from the north bank of the river. (HEW 2052)

SH19. River Teme Railway Bridge, Ludlow (SO517717) is the largest bridge on the Shrewsbury & Hereford Railway. It has a cast-iron single-span segmental arch which carries the railway line between Ludlow and Leominster over the River Teme, about two miles south of Ludlow. It is adjacent to the A49 road, from which it may be viewed by

parking at the junction with the B4361 just to the south of the river bridge and walking along the busy main road. The span of the bridge is 80 feet with brick abutments, and it has four ribs of I-section 30 inches deep. The arch ribs support a lattice of vertical and horizontal cast-iron members supporting the bridge deck. The bridge was completed in 1853, the designer being Henry Robertson. The contractors were Brassey and Field. The original structure had a timber deck, the double line of rails being carried on longitudinal waybeams. By 1921 the deck had been replaced in steel and in 1957 the structure was again repaired. (HEW 2053)

MARKET DRAYTON

SH20. Woodseaves Cutting (SJ 692323 to SJ 701299). In designing the Birmingham & Liverpool Junction Canal, Thomas Telford, its Engineer, used techniques more related to railway building than to traditional canals. There are high embankments and deep cuttings, of which Woodseaves Cutting is a typical example. Situated on the canal about 2½ miles south of Market Drayton, it is about 2,900 yards long and up to 70ft deep with steep side slopes. The waterway is narrowed in the deepest section of the cutting, presumably to reduce the amount of excavation required, and it is not possible for two narrow boats to pass within this section. There are four bridges along the length of the cutting, two of which are of a most unusual design with a small arch at the top of extremely high-sided walls and are probably unique to this canal. The contractor for this section of the canal was William Provis. Unfortunately Thomas Telford died before the canal was completed and William Cubitt deputised for him from February 1833 until the canal was completely opened in March 1835. The steep sides of the cutting have been a constant problem due to slippage of the unstable ground. (HEW 2070)

91 Woodseaves Cutting and high bridge, Birmingham & Liverpool Junction Canal.

MONTFORD BRIDGE

SH21. Montford Bridge (SJ 432153), which until recently carried the A5 Holyhead Road over the River Severn west of Shrewsbury, is a major landmark in the career of Thomas Telford. One of his first tasks following his arrival in Shrewsbury in 1786 was to design and oversee the building of a new bridge at Montford Bridge, this thus becoming the first bridge built to his own design. He commenced the design in 1790 and the bridge was opened on Lady Day 1792. Built in the local red sandstone, it has three segmental arches of 50, 58 and 50ft and was originally 20ft wide. The construction of the bridge was supervised by Matthew Davidson and the contractors were John Carline and John Tilley. Telford's bridge successfully withstood the disastrous flood of 1795 that carried away many of the bridges over the Severn. In 1963 the Shropshire county council widened the carriageway to the then standard width of 22ft and at the same time provided new footways. The design called for a new reinforced concrete slab which was cantilevered 5ft 6in beyond the each side of the original bridge. In the 1980s the bridge was again refurbished, with new concrete cantilevers being built. The A5 road now follows the new Montford Bridge bypass and the bridge only carries local traffic. (HEW 333)

92 Plaque commemorating Thomas Telford, Montford Bridge.

SHREWSBURY

SH22. Bage's Mill (SJ 500140) is the earliest surviving iron-framed mill building in Britain. It was built between 1796 and 1797 as a flax mill. The partners in this enterprise were Benjamin Benyon, a Shrewsbury wine merchant; John Marshall, a Leeds manufacturer; and Charles Bage, who was somewhat of an inventor and was commissioned to design the mill, the other two partners putting up the money. Bage had already been greatly influenced by Thomas Telford and knew well the Coalbrookdale Ironworks. His aim was to design a 'fireproof' building. He was at this time in correspondence with William Strutt of Derby, as can be seen from a collection of correspondence between Bage and Strutt in the Shrewsbury Library. The mill is

93 *Bage's Mill, Shrewsbury.*

sited close to the Shrewsbury Canal at Ditherington, then a village 1½ miles north of the city centre. Traditionally designed mill buildings with timber beams and floors were notorious for catching fire and Charles Bage designed his mill to be resistant to fire, with cast-iron columns and beams between which are brick arches to support the solid floor above. The iron columns and beams were probably cast at Coalbrookdale. The mill has five floors and is 177ft long and 39ft wide. The building was later used as a maltings but fell into disuse and its future was in some doubt. It has now been purchased by English Heritage and is to be restored. It is on private land but can be viewed from the A5191 road at Ditherington. (HEW 425)

SH23. Belvidere Railway Bridge (SJ 520125) is an elegant example of cast-iron railway bridge building. The railway line between Wolverhampton and Shrewsbury was built by the Shrewsbury and Birmingham Railway and opened in 1849. To carry the line across the River Severn to the east of Shrewsbury, a fine cast-iron arch bridge was built to the design of William Baker. The contractors were Messrs Hammond & Murray and the

94 *Belvidere Railway Bridge over River Severn, Shrewsbury.*

ironwork was cast at Coalbrookdale. The bridge has two skew spans of 101ft 6in each span having six segmental arch ribs, the bridge deck supported by a cast-iron lattice. There are massive stone piers with pilasters rising to deck level. In 1984 the bridge was extensively repaired and a new concrete deck was provided over the cast-iron floor plates; new parapets were provided and the bridge was repainted. The bridge can be reached by a 500-yard walk along the towpath of the river from Crowmere Road, Monkmoor at SJ 518129. (HEW 1703)

SH24. Castle Walk Footbridge (SJ 499130) was the first prestressed, post-tensioned concrete balanced cantilever bridge with a suspended mid-span to be built in Shropshire. Constructed in 1951 over the River Severn, it replaced a suspension bridge which had become unsafe due to corrosion. The main span of the bridge is 150ft with two side spans of 33ft. The designers of the bridge were L.G. Mouchel with the Prestressed Concrete Co. and the contractor was Taylor Woodrow Construction Ltd. (HEW 1105)

SH25. Coleham Pumping Station (SJ 496121) on the south bank of the River Severn at Coleham in Shrewsbury is a good preserved example of the work of the Victorian public health engineer. It was erected as part of the Shrewsbury sewerage and drainage scheme of 1896-1901. The engineers for the project were John Taylor & Son & Santa Crimp of London. The foundation stone was laid in 1898 and the building completed and opened on 1 January 1901. The main building, housing the engines, is a two-storey red brick building with a lower boiler house at its rear. There is an imposing chimney, nicely decorated. Within the main building are two beam engines which powered the pumps. They were built by Messrs. Renshaw and are dated 1900. They are compound rotative engines and run at a steam pressure of 90lbs per square inch provided by two Cornish boilers. The engines each have a high- and low-pressure cylinder connected to one end of the overhead beam with a crankshaft and flywheel 16ft in diameter and weighing 10 tons at the other end. Each stroke of the engines pumped 114 gallons of water. Under the sewerage scheme the town's sewage was collected by main collecting sewers then piped under the river to the pumping station. From there it was pumped to the new sewage works at Monkmoor to the north east of the town. The station ceased working in 1970 and is now preserved. It is open to visitors from time to time. (HEW 424)

SH26. The English Bridge (SJ 496124) has an interesting history of rebuilding. The road following the original route of Telford's Holyhead Road through Shrewsbury crosses the River Severn twice within the town. The eastern crossing is the English Bridge. The first bridge here was a five-arch structure of 1550 which was replaced in 1774 by a new masonry arch bridge designed by John Gwynn, a Shrewsbury architect. The bridge had seven spans, the largest, central, span being 54ft 6in, and was built in local Grinshill sandstone. In 1925 it was decided to completely rebuild the bridge under the direction of Arthur Ward, the borough surveyor. During the rebuilding a temporary timber bridge was built alongside the old bridge on the upstream side. The old structure was demolished and the stones were re-dressed and re-used. The bridge was widened from its

95　*Castle Walk Footbridge, Shrewsbury.*

96　*Beam Engine, Coleham Pumping Station.*

97　*The English Bridge, Shrewsbury.*

98 *Greyfriars Bridge, Shrewsbury .*

99 *Kingsland Bridge, Shrewsbury.*

100 *Porthill Bridge, Shrewsbury.*

original width of 15ft to 50ft between the parapets, but the original configuration of the bridge was maintained although the overall height of the bridge was reduced. The rebuilt bridge was opened in October 1927. (HEW 1027)

SH27. Greyfriars Bridge (SJ495121) Between the English Bridge and the Welsh Bridge in Shrewsbury the River Severn is crossed by several bridges. One is Greyfriars Bridge, a lattice girder bridge of wrought iron carried on masonry piers. The bridge, which spans 150ft, was constructed by Cochrane of Dudley in 1879. It is a footbridge with a width of six feet. It cost £2,500. It can be viewed from the river bank path. (HEW 1104)

SH28. Kingsland Bridge (SJ 488121) was the largest-span bridge in the region until 1966. It was opened in July 1882 and carries vehicular traffic over the River Severn. It has a single-span wrought-iron arch on masonry piers spanning 212ft. The roadway deck is carried about a third of the height of the arch. It is a private toll bridge owned by the Shrewsbury (Kingsland) Bridge Company. The Engineer was Henry Robertson, the MP for Shrewsbury at that time, and the bridge was constructed by the Cleveland Bridge and Engineering Company of Darlington. (HEW 1103)

SH29. Porthill Bridge (SJ485126) is one of the few examples of suspension bridge building in the region. It is a single-span steel wire rope suspension bridge with wrought-iron lattice towers carrying a footway across the River Severn in Shrewsbury. There are two cables on each side of the bridge, which has lattice girder parapets to stiffen it against wind-induced oscillation. The bridge spans 180ft and is 10ft wide. The designer was David Rowell & Co. Ltd of London and it was opened on 18 January 1923. (HEW 1102)

SH30. Welsh Bridge (SJ 489127). This major bridge is the second of the two crossings of the River Severn in Shrewsbury by the original route of the Holyhead Road, the other being the English Bridge (see above). The bridge has five arches built in local Grinshill sandstone. The centre span is 46ft 2in, the remaining

spans are all 43ft 4in. The bridge was designed and built between 1792 and 1794 by John Carline and John Tilley. John Carline was a stonemason and architect who came to Shrewsbury to be foreman mason during the rebuilding of the English Bridge. He leased the Grinshill quarries and supplied the stone for Atcham Bridge (see above). He became associated with John Tilley about 1789 and the two worked on the building of Montford Bridge (see above) and other bridges in the area. A notable feature of the Welsh Bridge is the inclusion of a horizontal pulley wheel at the base of the downstream parapet. This was used to haul barges up the river over the shallows downstream of the bridge, the Severn at that time being navigable well above Shrewsbury. (HEW 1025)

101 *The Welsh Bridge, Shrewsbury.*

TELFORD

SH31. Albert Edward Bridge (SJ 661038), a near twin to Victoria Bridge at Arley, is one of the largest remaining spans in cast iron in Britain. It carries the double track of the railway line to Ironbridge power station over the River Severn. It has a single cast-iron arch of 201ft span with four ribs, each made up from nine segments with bolted joints. The ribs have an I-section and are 26in deep. It was opened on 1 November 1864 and is thought to be the last major cast-iron railway bridge to have been built. It was designed by Sir John Fowler and erected by Brassey and Field. The ironwork was cast nearby by the Coalbrookdale Company. Sir John Fowler had a long and distinguished career in civil engineering and was the youngest ever President of the Institution of Civil Engineers when elected in 1865. He was the designer of many bridges and viaducts in masonry and iron and is perhaps best remembered for being responsible, with Benjamin Baker (later Sir Benjamin Baker), for the design of the Forth Railway Bridge, the first major structure to be built in steel which opened in 1890. Albert Edward Bridge is most impressive in its setting, with the steep wooded sides of the Severn Gorge forming a backdrop. The bridge can be viewed from the river bank footpath, accessed from the car park at Dale End Riverside Park near the junction between the Wharfage and Station Road. (HEW 350)

102 *Albert Edward Bridge.*

SH32. Hadley Park Locks (SJ 672133) are the only surviving canal locks with guillotine gates in the county. In the area now occupied by Telford there was a network of small canals which, until the opening of the branch canal from Norbury junction on the Birmingham & Liverpool Junction Canal to Wappenshall junction in 1835, was isolated from the national canal system. One of these canals was the Shrewsbury Canal and at Hadley Park a series of unusual locks was constructed by its Engineer, Josiah Clowes.

103 *(Right) Hadley Park Locks.*

104 *(Far right) Madeley Church, Telford.*

The locks had conventional top gates but the lower gates were of the guillotine type. The gate was raised vertically by chains with a counterbalance weight over the tail of the lock. The locks were built about 1793. There were originally about 11 similar locks on the Shrewsbury Canal with slightly differing mechanisms. The locks, now very dilapidated, can be viewed by walking up the line of the canal from the A442 road or from the nearby housing estate. (HEW 938)

SH33. St Michael's Church, Madeley (SO 696041). The old village church of Madeley, now a part of Telford New Town, is an unusual building designed by Thomas Telford and completed in 1796. The building is octagonal in plan with a square tower inset into the west wall. There are two tiers of windows, rectangular in the lower tier and arched in the upper. The interior of the church reflects Telford's desire, as also exhibited at St Mary Magdalene at Bridgnorth (see above), for a large unobstructed space. The original internal plan was rectangular with triangular vestries cutting off the corners of the octagon at the east end and a timber gallery on three sides. The roof structure is of interest, having paired timber trusses from which the ceiling is suspended by metal hangers. A circular stone staircase in the tower gives access to the gallery and bell chamber. In 1910 the east wall of the church was extended eastwards to form an elongated chancel, the original east window being replaced in the new wall. An almost identical church was built some years later by Telford at Malinslee (see below). (HEW 1333)

SH34. St Leonards Church, Malinslee (SJ 689081) is the youngest of the three major churches designed by Thomas Telford in the county. Nine years after designing the church at Madeley (see above), Thomas Telford repeated the design, on a slightly smaller scale, for the new church at Malinslee dedicated to St Leonard. This is another octagonal building but this time without any later alterations, thus preserving the pure octagon. As at Madeley there is a square tower on the west side. The tower has a

105 *Malinslee Church, Telford.*

clock with three faces which was replaced in 1949. The interior of the church is again rectangular, with two triangular rooms at the east end and a gallery round three sides with stone and cast-iron columns. The interior of the tower is circular with a doorway leading into the church. (HEW 1780)

WHITCHURCH

SH35. Whitchurch Station Footbridge (SO 550417) is an interesting footbridge, recently renovated, which carries a public footpath crossing the running lines and site of the former goods yard just north of Whitchurch station. Unusually for such a location, it is a suspension bridge with a main span of 120ft between the towers and side spans of 27ft. The suspension chains are made up from vertical wrought-iron flat bars three inches deep and one inch thick. The bars are about 12ft long and are joined into a chain with pin joints. There are two bars to each link of the chain, alternate links having the bars strapped together or separated by a two-inch gap. At the joints there are horizontal rods spanning the full width of the bridge and bolted at the ends. There are 10 bays in the main span and four bays in each side span. The ends of the suspension chains are anchored by a complex arrangement of three near-vertical iron rods between

106 *Whitchurch Station Footbridge.*

11 and 15ft long, buried in the ground. The bridge deck is suspended by vertical and inclined hangers from the joints in the suspension chains. Each of the main towers is formed from two vertical timber columns 13in square. The base of each column rests in a cast-iron shoe with a horizontal rod forming a pinned joint. The outside of each shoe is protected by a substantial masonry block, presumably to prevent damage to the base of the tower by vehicles using the goods yard. Below the deck level the two towers at each end are cross-braced by two 7in-square timbers. Access to the bridge is by means of a flight of steps at each end. The bridge has recently been refurbished. (HEW 2167)

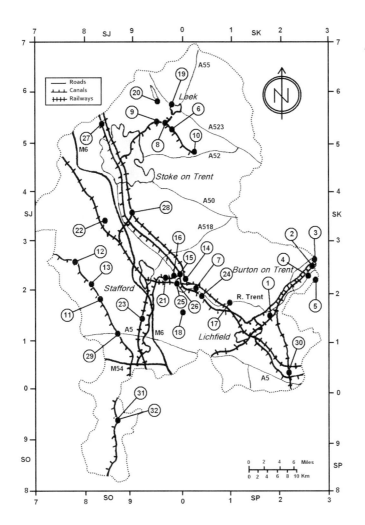

Map of Staffordshire (ST).

ST 1. Chetwynd Bridge, Alrewas
ST 2. Claymills Pumping Station
ST 3. Dove Aqueduct
ST 4. Stapenhill Suspension Bridge
ST 5. Winshill Water Tower, Burton upon Trent
ST 6. Cheddleton Mill
ST 7. Wolseley Bridge, Colwich
ST 8. Hazlehurst Aqueduct
ST 9. Hazlehurst Iron Bridge
ST10. Froghall Basin
ST11. Cowley Cutting and Tunnel
ST12. Grub Street Cutting, Gnosall
ST13. Shelmore Bank, Gnosall
ST14. Essex Bridge, Gt Haywood
ST15. Canal Junction Bridge, Gt Haywood
ST16. Trent Aqueduct, Gt Haywood

ST17. High Bridge, Mavesyn Ridware
ST18. Pye Green Water Tower, Hednesford
ST19. Brindley Mill, Leek
ST20. Rudyard Lake
ST21. Milford Aqueduct
ST22. Milmeece Pumping Station
ST23. Penkridge Viaduct
ST24. Trent Aqueduct, Rugeley
ST25. Shugborough Hall Bridges
ST26. Shugborough Tunnel
ST27. Harecastle Tunnels, Stoke on Trent
ST28. Stone Railway Station
ST29. Stretton Aqueduct
ST30. Anker Viaduct, Tamworth
ST31. Bratch Locks, Wombourne
ST32. Bratch Pumping Station, Wombourne

ALREWAS

ST1.Chetwynd Bridge (SK 187139) is a cast-iron arch bridge designed by Joseph Potter, the County Surveyor, carrying the A513 Alrewas-to-Tamworth road over the River Tame near its confluence with the River Trent. It is also known as Salter's Bridge. There are three segmental arches with spans of just under 65ft, 75ft and 65ft respectively. The spandrel space between the arch and roadway is filled with an X-lattice and the bridge has massive stone piers and abutments. The northern arch is over dry land. A plaque on the bridge records that it was erected by the County of Stafford in 1824. The ironwork was probably cast at Coalbrookdale. In 1979 an inspection revealed that the bridge was affected by severe corrosion and fracturing of some elements and a major refurbishment was undertaken, completed in 1983. (HEW 168)

107 Chetwynd Bridge.

BURTON UPON TRENT

ST2.Claymills Pumping Station (SK 263258). This large and important preserved pumping station was built to pump raw sewage from the end of the outfall sewer from Burton upon Trent to a sewage treatment farm 2¼ miles away. Parliamentary powers were obtained in 1880; construction commenced in 1884 and was completed in 1885. There are two main buildings, each housing two Woolf compound beam engines and a boiler house containing five Lancashire boilers. Each engine powered two ram pumps, one driven from the end of the beam and the other from the tail rod of the high-pressure cylinder. The engines were built by Gimson & Company of Leicester and are dated 1885. Each engine has two cylinders, a high-pressure cylinder of 24in bore and six-foot stroke, and a low-pressure cylinder of 38in bore and eight-foot stroke. The steam passes first into the high-pressure cylinder from which it is exhausted into the low-pressure cylinder. Steam pressure is 80lb per square inch. The beam drives a crank which carries a 24ft-diameter flywheel weighing 24 tons. There are several ancillary buildings on the site including a well-equipped workshop and an electricity-generating plant, which was installed in 1890 in the boiler house but moved to its present location in 1937 when the original boilers were replaced. In 1993 the station was handed over to the Claymills Pumping Engines Trust who have restored the two engines in the north engine house to working order. The site is open to the public at weekends and steaming days are held from time to time. (HEW 2054)

108 Beam engine at Claymills Pumping Station.

ST3. Dove Aqueduct (SK 268269). Just east of Burton upon Trent the Trent & Mersey Canal crosses the River Dove by means of a brick aqueduct with 12 low segmental arches of 15ft 4in span. The arch ring is 24in thick and exhibits a lack of bonding between the brickwork at about

109 *River Dove Aqueduct on the Trent & Mersey Canal.*

110 *Stapenhill Bridge, Burton upon Trent.*

111 *Winshill Water Tower, Burton upon Trent.*

one third of the depth of the arch ring. The considerable strength of the structure is required since the canal is carried across the aqueduct complete with its puddled clay bed. Its designer was James Brindley and it was built between 1768 and 1770. The aqueduct can be viewed by walking along the towpath from the A5121 road to the west (SK 262266). (HEW 1699)

ST4. Stapenhill Suspension Bridge (SK 253219) is a suspension footbridge with an unusual cable formation and an associated approach viaduct over the River Trent between the town of Burton upon Trent on the north bank and Stapenhill on the south bank. The main span of the bridge is 120ft with two side spans of 60ft. The design of the two wrought-iron cables from which the bridge deck is suspended is of interest, as each is formed from three flat wrought-iron plates, 8in wide and half an inch thick, riveted together to give a cable 1½in thick. Each plate is 18ft long but the joints between the plates are staggered to give one joint every six feet. The towers are also unusual. Below deck level they are circular cast-iron columns, whereas above deck level they are square cast-iron with decorative ribbing. The deck passes between each pair of towers. The date 1889 is cast into the cable tower portals with the inscription 'THE GIFT OF MICHAEL ARTHUR FIRST BARON BURTON'. The designer of the bridge was A.A. Langley, Chief Engineer of the Midland Railway and the contractor was Thornewill & Warham of Burton upon Trent. To the north of the bridge, across the low-lying ground between the bridge and the town, is a viaduct 560 yards long with 81 spans. (HEW 1785)

ST5. Winshill Water Tower (SK 265227) is a large prominent blue brick building with red brick corners and decorative facings, which stands on high ground overlooking Burton upon Trent. The tank is slightly larger than the tower below and the brickwork is corbelled out to suit. The tower is about 90ft tall and is pierced by windows on three levels. It is owned by the South Staffordshire Water company and a coat of arms is placed over the door-way .There is a large number of radio aerials fixed to the top of the tower. It is not accessible to the public but can be viewed from the appropriately named Tower Road alongside.

CHEDDLETON

ST6. Cheddleton Mill (SJ 973526). At the village of Cheddleton, located between the River Churnet and the Caldon Canal, is a rare example of a pair of water-powered mills used latterly for grinding flints for use in the nearby pottery industry. The river supplied the power and the canal brought in the raw flints and carried away the finished product. Both mills are powered by low breast water wheels. The South Mill is the older of the two mills and was originally used for grinding corn, being converted to flint grinding at an unknown date. The North Mill was built for grinding flint and dates from before 1783. It may have associations with James Brindley. Both mills have two-storey brick buildings with the mill wheel mounted externally. The South Mill wheel is 20ft 5in diameter, the North Mill has a 22ft-diameter wheel. The mills are now preserved by a trust and are open to the public at weekends and at other times by arrangement. (HEW 1133)

112 Cheddleton Mills.

COLWICH

ST7. Wolseley Bridge (SK 021204) is a large masonry arch bridge with an interesting history, as a bridge was recorded at this site, where the road from Rugeley to Stone (now the A51) crosses the River Trent, in the 12th century. The county took over responsibility for the bridge in 1710 but in February 1795 a flood destroyed or severely damaged a number of bridges in the area, Wolseley Bridge being reported 'out of repair' at the Easter Quarter Sessions. John Rennie submitted a design for a new bridge in 1797 and work was commenced by builders James Trubshaw & Sons of nearby Colwich. At the time James Trubshaw was also the county bridge surveyor. They did not, however, complete the work and in 1799 it was agreed to make payments direct to Trubshaw's subcontractors. Prior to this, in April 1799 John Varley entered into a contract to complete the bridge for £5,110 but Rennie, who was super-vising the work, considered it substandard and in April 1800 refused to make any further pay-ments. Varley abandoned the contract and the work was completed by Joseph Potter, who had been appointed in 1800 to be surveyor of county bridges for the county of Stafford. Wolseley Bridge is a nicely designed three-arch bridge in sandstone obtained from the estate of Sir William Wolseley at nearby Wolseley Hall. The arches are segmental with spans of 52ft 6in, 57ft and 52ft 6in. The arch ring is 36in thick. There are decorative niches with rounded heads above the cutwaters on each of the piers. (HEW 1786)

113 Wolseley Bridge.

DENFORD

ST8. Hazlehurst Aqueduct (SJ 954537) is a relatively rare example of an aqueduct carrying one canal over another. To the west of Hazlehurst the Leek Branch of the Caldon Canal, opened in 1802, leaves the main line of the canal to the south. Beyond the junction the main line descends to a lower level by means of the three locks at Hollinshurst following which the branch canal curves northwards and passes over the main line by a brick aqueduct. The aqueduct has a single span with a semi-circular arch 15in thick. The skew span is about 27ft. The aqueduct bears a commemorative inscription on both sides reading 'Hazlehurst Aqueduct 1841'. This date is much later than the opening of the branch since the present arrangement of the two canals is the second to exist at the site, the previous arrangement with a simple junction followed by a flight of three locks on the main line having been found unsatisfactory. The aqueduct can be visited by walking along the towpath of the main line of the canal from the east where a minor road crosses the lower canal (SJ 956535). There is a flight of steps linking the upper and lower levels. (HEW 554)

ST9. Hazlehurst Iron Bridge (SJ 948537). At the entrance to the top lock of the Hollinshurst flight a 24ft-span cast-iron arch bridge carries the towpath of the Leek Branch of the Caldon Canal over the main line. The two arch ribs are cast in two sections with a bolted joint at the centre. The parapet rail is cast integrally with the ribs and filled with interlocking semi-circles. The bridge is dated 1842, the date of the final alteration of the configuration of the junction. See also Hazlehurst Aqueduct above. (HEW 857)

114 *Hazlehurst Lock Bridge, Caldon Canal.*

FROGHALL

ST10. Froghall Basin (SK 027477), with its associated inclined planes, was the terminal basin of the Caldon Canal from its opening in 1783 until the extension of the canal to Uttoxeter in 1807. Froghall Basin was an important interchange point, with limestone being carried down by tramway from Caldon Low quarries some 650ft above the canal. The original terminus of the canal was south of the B5053 road and was opened in late 1778 or 1779. The canal was extended a few years later through a 76-yard tunnel to its present site just beyond the Froghall to Foxt road. The basin has one short and one long arm and there are a number of canal-side buildings associated with the canal including a cottage and stables. Along the east side of the basin there are extensive lime kilns. Traces can be seen of the tramways that served the quarries above. The first tramway was built in 1779 to the original terminus at the time of the opening of the canal. Its route is now difficult to trace. In 1783 a second tramway was built from the new terminus. Following reports by John Rennie, an Act of 1802 authorised a third tramway running further to the south through the village of Whiston. In 1847 the canal was purchased by the North Staffordshire Railway and in 1849 a fourth and final tramway was built which partly followed the route of the 1783 tramway but took a much more direct course. The route of this final tramway, although long derelict, can still be traced on the ordnance map. All the tramways operated with self-acting inclines and more level sections in between. The basin area is now a picnic site but much still remains to be seen. In 2005 the first lock on the route of the canal to Uttoxeter was excavated and rebuilt and now leads to a small basin. (HEW 1590)

115 Froghall Basin, Caldon Canal.

GNOSALL

ST11. Cowley Cutting & Tunnel (SJ 829190 to SJ 822201) When planning the route of the Birmingham & Liverpool Junction Canal it was the intention of Thomas Telford, its Engineer, to drive a tunnel 690 yards long through the high ground south-west of Gnosall Heath. In the summer of 1830 William Provis, the contractor for this section of the canal, began driving the tunnel, starting at the north end. After about 90 yards had been driven a serious fault in the rock was discovered and although driving continued for a further 150 yards the condition of the rock was such that further tunnelling was abandoned. It was decided to open out the remainder of the proposed tunnel and also open out about 160 yards of the tunnel already driven. This gave rise to the situation seen today with a long, deep cutting from the south about 1,300 yards long followed by a short 81-yard tunnel. The cutting has steep side slopes and a maximum depth of about 40ft. The tunnel is cut through sandstone and is unlined except for a length of about 13ft at the south end which has side walls and an arch in masonry. The towpath is continued through the tunnel, a characteristic of Telford's canal tunnels. (HEW 2166)

116 Grub Street Cutting and Bridge, Birmingham & Liverpool Junction Canal.

ST12. Grub Street Cutting (SJ 778255 to SJ 792234) is another example of the deep cuttings on the Birmingham & Liverpool Junction Canal and is similar to Woodseaves and Cowley cuttings described previously. It is about 2,900 yards long with steep side slopes and the maximum depth is about 40 to 50 feet. The canal's Engineer was Thomas Telford and the contractor for this section of the canal was William Provis. The cutting follows a curved alignment and is crossed by three bridges. Two of the bridges are of the pattern unique to this canal, with small-span semi-circular arches at the top of high vertical abutment walls. The southernmost bridge, High Bridge number 39, is of this form but at some time a double arch in brickwork has been inserted about halfway up the abutment walls, presumably to resist a tendency for the walls to move inwards. The short telegraph pole on top of the arch is a surviving remnant of the telegraph

wires which ran along the canal, the wires passing underneath the bridge arch. Grub Street Cutting was completed by about 1832 but the complete opening of the canal was delayed by problems at Shelmore Bank (see below) and did not take place until March 1835. (HEW 2062)

ST13. Shelmore Bank (SJ 805215 to SJ 793228) is a notable earthwork on the Birmingham & Liverpool Junction Canal. The line of the canal takes a wide curve to the west between Norbury junction and Gnosall Heath. This curve was necessary to avoid the canal passing through the land surrounding Norbury Park, the seat of Lord Anson. To accommodate the deviation it was necessary to build a long, high, embankment, causing serious difficulties in construction and delaying the complete opening of the canal. Shelmore Bank is 1,900 yards long and up to 60ft high. Construction started in late summer of 1829 but great difficulty was encountered in stabilising the fill material, and settlement and slippage of the bank continued despite all efforts. Tipping of material continued accompanied by the spreading of the bank as the material settled but by the end of 1832 only 300 yards of the canal over the bank had been puddled. It was not finally completed until July 1835, the remainder of the canal having been open since March. The problems encountered in stabilising the bank can still be observed in the very flat side slopes. The embankment is pierced by two road bridges and a stream culvert. Owing to the great width of the bank the road bridges are more akin to short tunnels, the northernmost 'tunnel' being 150ft long. There are stop gates at both ends of the embankment which close automatically in the event of a breach in the canal over the bank. Thomas Telford, the canal's Engineer, was ill in the latter stages of construction and William Cubitt deputised for him from February 1833. (HEW 1224)

GREAT HAYWOOD

ST14. Essex Bridge (SJ 995226) An early 18th-century multi-arch bridge. This long pedestrian bridge crosses the River Trent south of Great Haywood village. It possibly dates from the late 16th century, being built by the Earl of Essex to transport his horses and hounds to nearby Cannock Chase. Today the sandstone bridge, which was rebuilt in 1729-33 by Richard Trubshaw, has 14 arches, although it is possible that the original bridge was much longer. The arches are segmental with a single course of stone voussoirs 14in deep, the spans varying between 14 and 15 feet. The stone piers have cutwaters extending up to the pathway on both sides of the bridge to form pedestrian refuges. At the south end the bridge turns sharply, the 13th arch being curved in plan. The width of the pathway is about 4ft 3in. The bridge can be reached either from Great Haywood to the north or from Shugborough Park to the south. (HEW 1132)

ST15. Canal Junction Bridge (SJ 995229) is a much illustrated Brindley canal bridge with a very flat arch for its time. Just west of Great Haywood, the Staffordshire & Worcestershire Canal makes a junction with the Trent & Mersey Canal. In order to carry the towpath of the Trent & Mersey Canal over the junction, James Brindley built a red brick arch bridge of unusual proportions. Although the bridge has a span of 35ft 6in the rise of the segmental arch is only about six feet, giving a span-to-rise ratio of about six, which is unusually flat. The arch ring is 13in thick and is surmounted by a course of stone blocks and there is a stone 'keystone'. It was built about 1771-2, this section of the Staffordshire & Worcestershire Canal being the last to be completed. Cast-iron rubbing strakes are mounted on the corners of the bridge abutments and on the parapet wall corner to prevent damage to the brickwork by towropes passing round the corners. All the strakes show much evidence of grooving by towropes. The bridge may be viewed by following the towpath of the Trent & Mersey Canal westwards from the bridge at Great Haywood village. (HEW 676)

ST16. Trent Aqueduct (SJ 994229). Just south of its junction with the Trent & Mersey Canal the Staffordshire & Worcestershire Canal crosses the River Trent. Here James Brindley built a stone aqueduct with four spans, completed about 1772. The span of the arches is about 21ft. The 12ft-wide waterway is flanked by wide grassed areas. The aqueduct was built by Bindley's technique of building the structure on dry land and then diverting the river through it. Between the aqueduct and the canal junction there is a single arch over the site of a tail race from a nearby mill. (HEW 885)

HANDSACRE

ST17. High Bridge (SK 092168), carrying the B5014 road over the River Trent near Rugeley, is a major cast-iron single-span arch bridge with a remarkable recent history. It was completed in 1831, the ironwork being supplied by the Coalbrookdale Company. The designer of the bridge was Joseph Potter who was also responsible for Chetwynd Bridge (see above). The span of the bridge is 140ft and the overall width 25ft 8in. The arch has five ribs, each made of from seven segments with bolted joints. The ribs are 36in deep and two inches thick. The space between the arch and the deck is filled with intersecting struts and lateral stiffness is provided by circular tie bars. The stone abutments incorporate decorative low stone towers with massive stone caps. The bridge stood unchanged until 1982 when it was threatened by anticipated mining subsidence. A major operation was launched to safeguard the bridge while the subsidence took place. The road was diverted onto a Bailey bridge erected alongside to the west and concrete piers were constructed in the river supporting a new steel arch immediately underneath the iron ribs. The bridge was lightened by removing the road pavement and the parapets. The weight of the cast-iron arch was then transferred to the steel arch by flat jacks placed between the two arches, packing then being inserted. Subsequently a new bridge was built alongside to the west and the old bridge restored for pedestrian use. The temporary supports were then removed. (HEW 726)

117 Essex Bridge, Great Haywood.

118 Towpath Bridge at junction with Staffs. & Worcs. Canal and Trent & Mersey Canal.

119 High Bridge, Mavesyn Ridware.

HEDNESFORD

ST18. Pye Green Water Tower (SJ 989144) This 60,000-gallon concrete water tower was built in 1935 by the South Staffordshire Water Company and has an unusual feature. It was anticipated that the tower would be affected during its lifetime by mining subsidence and precautions were taken in the design of the tower to accommodate any subsequent movement. The main structure is 50ft high and octagonal in shape. Hidden within the external walls of the tower is extra stiffening by circumferential bracing and the tank itself is stiffened by bracing struts. Provision was made for the insertion of hydraulic jacks at the base of the tower which would enable any tilting to be corrected. Although the tower eventually settled by 2ft 8in the jacking system was not required as the tower remained vertical.

LEEK

ST19. Brindley Mill (SJ 978570) is a preserved water mill with associations with James Brindley. In Leek, on the A523 road about a quarter of a mile north-west of the town centre, is an interesting water mill dating from 1752. The mill lies on the River Churnet which powers an undershot water wheel 16ft diameter with 40 oak paddles. Within the stone mill building there were originally three sets of millstones, but there are now only two, one of which is still operational. The main pit wheel is cast in two halves and has 116 teeth, the wallower gear has 50 teeth and the main vertical shaft is in oak, with an 18in diameter and a brass footstep bearing. The mill has three floors with the stones on the second floor, fed from hoppers on the third floor. It is believed that the mill was built by James Brindley a few years before his involvement with canal building for which he is so well known. Later in the life of the mill a turbine was installed in the bypass waterway. The mill operated as a corn mill until 1940 when it was abandoned, but in 1970 the Brindley Mill Preservation Trust was set up and the restored mill was opened on 4 May 1974. It is open to visitors on some weekends. (HEW 2161)

120 *(Below) Pye Green Water Tower, Hednesford.*

121 *(Below right) Waterwheel at Brindley Mill, Leek.*

ST20. Rudyard Lake (SJ 952583) is a major canal reservoir with an unusual spillway. Nearly two miles long, it was built by John Rennie to supply water to the Caldon Canal. It has a 30ft-high earth dam at the south-eastern end of the lake with a puddled clay core. The original masonry weir and the spillway, which is of an uncommon design

and was completed in 1801, still stands. The original specification for the reservoir is held by Staffordshire Moorlands District Council. In it Rennie states that the embankment must be in the form of a horizontal arch, 40ft wide at the top with the clay puddle in the centre, which is 12ft wide at the bottom and six feet wide at the top. The reservoir, while still supplying water to the canal has become a popular tourist attraction and there is a narrow-gauge steam railway running along the eastern shore of the lake. It was a condition of permission for the reservoir that the feeder channel was navigable as far as Leek. (HEW 1472)

MILFORD

ST21. Milford Aqueduct (SJ 973215) is sited where the Staffordshire & Worcestershire Canal crosses the River Sow. Built by James Brindley in c.1772, it is a low brick structure with four arches of 22ft span. As with the nearby Trent Aqueduct (see above) the aqueduct was built on dry land and the river diverted to flow through it. The arches are segmental with four half-brick rings and a stone course above. The rest of the aqueduct is in stone and the canal is flanked on both sides by wide grassed areas. There is a stone parapet wall on the east, towpath, side only. At both ends of the aqueduct the canal makes a sharp turn in order to cross the river at right angles. (HEW 974)

122 *Milford Aqueduct, Staffs. & Worcs. Canal.*

MILLMEECE

ST22. Millmeece Pumping Station (SJ 830339) is a steam-powered water pumping station with two relatively rare tandem compound steam engines preserved in working order. It was built to supply water for the Staffordshire Potteries Waterworks Company. The buildings house the two main pumping engines and several auxiliary steam engines. The main engines are both tandem compound engines with the high-pressure and low-pressure cylinders on a common piston rod. The older engine was installed in 1914 by Ashton Frost of Blackburn, Lancashire. The high-pressure cylinder is 26in diameter and the low-pressure cylinder 49in diameter with a five-foot stroke. It is rated at 308h. p. and has a flywheel 19ft 6in diameter weighing 31½ tons. The second engine was installed in 1927 by Hathorn Davey of Leeds. It is similar in form to the 1914 engine but with detailed differences. The cylinder diameters are 27in and 52in and it is rated at 380h.p. Steam is supplied from three Lancashire boilers which were fitted with automatic stokers in 1965. The water is extracted from two wells, each having two bore holes. Well No. 1 has bores 1,242ft and 533ft deep, Well No. 2 has bores 550ft and 530ft deep. The pumps were actuated by vertical pump rods from a large bell crank driven by a horizontal extension of the engine piston rod. The main station buildings, the engine house and the boiler house, are in red brick, nicely decorated, with slate roofs and were erected by Godwin & Sons of Hanley. The station was built 1913-14 and one engine was installed. Regular pumping started in 1919 and in

123 *Millmeece Water Pumping Station.*

1927 the second engine was installed. In 1938 electric pumps replaced the older engine but the 1927 engine ran until 1979 when electric pumps were substituted. The pumping station is leased to a Preservation Trust and is open to the public on most weekends. The engines are steamed about once per month. (HEW 2192)

PENKRIDGE

ST23. Penkridge Viaduct (SJ 921145) is a major structure on the Grand Junction Railway and was Thomas Brassey's first railway contract. On 6 May 1833 the Grand Junction Railway obtained its Act of Parliament for a line from Birmingham to the newly completed Liverpool & Manchester Railway at Newton le Willows. In order to cross the valley of the River Penk just north of Penkridge, an embankment and viaduct were required. The viaduct has seven arches each of 30ft span and carries the line 37ft above the river. The segmental arches are built in red brick with ashlar masonry fascias and are thickened in both directions near the base, giving the viaduct an unusual profile. The river passes through the third span from the south, the northernmost span crossing a minor road. There is a brick parapet wall above a stone moulding. The Engineer for the southern half of the line was originally George Stephenson but he was replaced in 1835 by Joseph Locke. This viaduct and an adjoining length of railway line was the first piece of railway construction undertaken by Thomas Brassey, who became the leading railway contractor of his time with projects all over the world. The line was opened on 4 July 1837 and the viaduct is still carrying main line traffic today. (HEW 520)

RUGELEY

ST24. Trent Aqueduct (SK 039195) North-west of Rugeley the Trent & Mersey Canal makes a crossing of the River Trent. The aqueduct is in blue brickwork with six arches of 21ft span. The river flows through the southernmost three arches, the northern arches being over dry land but used by the river in time of flood. The aqueduct is a typical Brindley structure with the massive arches required to carry the full weight of the canal including its puddled clay bed. The technique may be contrasted with the much lighter structures in iron developed later by Thomas Telford and others. (HEW 1719)

124 *Penkridge Viaduct, Grand Junction Railway.*

SHUGBOROUGH

ST25. Shugborough Hall Bridges (SJ 988224 & SJ 993227). In the grounds of Shugborough Hall are two fine bridges carrying footpaths over channels of the River Trent which are elegant examples of estate bridge building in cast iron. Both the bridges were cast by John Toye & Co. **The Blue Bridge** has three spans of segmental arches with spans of about 20ft. The 6in-deep arch ribs are of P-section and the space between the arch and the deck is filled with circles of decreasing diameter towards the centre of each span. The ribs and circles are cast in one piece. The abutments and piers are in sandstone ashlar and the deck is formed by cast-iron plates with an asphalt surface. In February 1795 a severe flood on the River Trent caused considerable damage and a new cut for the river was constructed about 1805. This left an island between the old and new branches of the river and the bridge was required for access to the island. It was built in 1813. (HEW 1788) **The Red Bridge** is a single arch of 42ft 6in span. Each of the two arch ribs is eight inches deep and the spandrel space is also filled with interlocking rings of decreasing size. It is painted red, giving rise to its name but it is also known as the 'Chinese' bridge as it gives access to a Chinese-style pavilion. (HEW 1787)

125   *The Blue Bridge, Shugborough Hall.*

ST26. Shugborough Tunnel (SJ 981216 to SJ 988216) is a double-track railway tunnel on a curved alignment with ornate portals which carries the Trent Valley railway under the Satnall Hills at Shugborough Park. It was the largest engineering work on the Trent Valley line which was built in 1846-7 as a direct line to the North between Rugby and Stafford, thus avoiding the route through Birmingham and Wolverhampton. The tunnel is 777 yards long and is brick-lined, having a semi-circular arch springing from vertical walls. The tunnel has ornate decorated portals in ashlar masonry with turrets and battlements designed to be in keeping with the follies in the Park. The joint engineers for the line were Robert Stephenson, George Bidder and Thomas Gooch and the contractors were Thomas Brassey, William Mackenzie and John Stephenson. Close access to the tunnel portals is not possible but the eastern portal can be viewed from Shugborough Park. (HEW 1126)

126   *The Red or Chinese Bridge, Shugborough Hall.*

STOKE ON TRENT

ST27. Harecastle Canal Tunnels (SJ 838543 to SJ 849517). The first of the two Harecastle tunnels was the first major transport tunnel to be built in Britain. The route of the Trent & Mersey Canal runs south from the valley of the River Weaver through high ground to the north of Stoke-on-Trent into the valley of the River Trent. A long tunnel was needed to carry the summit level of the canal under the hills at Harecastle. The original tunnel, one of five on the canal, was 2,880 yards long, largely brick-lined, and took

nine years to complete between 1766 and 1775. It was only wide enough for one narrow boat, being 8ft 6in wide at water level. Fifteen working shafts were used in its construction, giving a total of 32 working faces. It was driven through gritstone, limestone, and coal measures. Side tunnels were driven into the coal measures to extract minerals, and the water which entered the tunnel was used as part of the water supply for the summit level of the canal. The original Engineer for the tunnel was James Brindley until his death in 1772, after which Hugh Henshall took over. There was no towpath and boats had to be laboriously 'legged' through the tunnel. Between 1825 and 1827 a second, parallel, tunnel was dug under the direction of Thomas Telford just to the east of the old tunnel. This tunnel was slightly longer at 2,926 yards, and was of greater dimension, being 9ft 3in wide at water level with a towpath 4ft 6in wide which enabled boats to be hauled through the tunnel by horses. The contractors for the second tunnel were Daniel Pritchard and William Hoof and the resident engineer was James Potter. An indication of the progress made in tunnelling is apparent since the second tunnel, of larger dimensions, was driven in one quarter of the time taken for the original tunnel. For a while both

tunnels were in use, allowing two-way traffic, but both were damaged by mining subsidence and the original tunnel was closed to traffic and is now derelict. The second tunnel is still in use with a one-way traffic system in operation but its headroom has been reduced by subsidence. The profiles hanging at the entrances to the tunnel indicate the maximum height of boat allowed to enter the tunnel. At the southern end of the tunnel there is a forced draft ventilation system. (HEWs 54 & 465)

127 *North portals of Harecastle Tunnels, Trent & Mersey Canal.*

STONE

ST28. Stone Railway Station (SJ 897345) is nicely designed and typical of the stations erected by the North Staffordshire Railway and situated at the junction between the Stoke-on-Trent to Colwich main line and the branch from Stone to Norton Bridge. The North Staffs. Railway from Stoke to Stone together with the branch to the (then) Grand Junction Railway opened in April 1848. Originally the station had platforms facing onto both the main line and the branch but the main line platform has been removed. The main station building has two storeys in red brickwork with stone corners and a substantial sandstone moulding at first-floor level. The south elevation has three bays with Dutch gables surmounted by stone pinnacles. The two outer gables have stone recesses with heraldic shields. The gables are repeated on the north elevation but without the recesses. The building is extended to the north as a single storey with a flat roof. The architect for the station was Sir Henry Hunt. The station bears a remarkable similarity to the much larger station at Stoke-on-Trent and it is believed that another architect named R.A. Stent may have worked with Hunt on the design of that station. (HEW 1880)

STRETTON

ST29. Stretton Aqueduct (SJ 873107), a major structure on Telford's Birmingham & Liverpool Junction Canal, was constructed in 1832-3. It carries the line of the canal over the modern A5 road near the village of Stretton. The waterway is carried in a cast-iron trough formed of flanged plates in five sections, each 6ft 6in long bolted together and supported by six cast-iron arch ribs, each of which is cast in two sections and joined at the centre. The name of the designer, Thomas Telford, and the date of construction, 1835, are commemorated by an inscription cast on the centre panel of the trough. Close inspection reveals that the name of William Hazledine, the ironfounder, has been crudely filed off, it is believed in deference to the main contractor for this section of the canal, John Wilson & Sons. There is an almost identical aqueduct at Nantwich, also by Telford, and a similar one at Congleton, nominally by William Crosley. (HEW 228)

128 *Stone station, Trent Valley Railway.*

TAMWORTH

ST30. River Anker Viaduct (SK 213036) is an impressive masonry viaduct on an early main line railway. In 1836 the Birmingham & Derby Junction Railway was authorised to construct a line from Stechford (near Birmingham on the London & Birmingham Railway) to Derby via Tamworth and Burton upon Trent. The line was opened on 12 August 1839, but to a junction with the London and Birmingham Railway at Hampton-in-Arden instead of Stechford. At Tamworth the line crosses the low-lying ground near the River Anker on an embankment and a viaduct of 19 arches. The viaduct has 18 segmental arches of 30ft span and a single segmental skew arch of 60ft span. The total length is about 715ft and the line is about 45ft above the river. It has stone piers and brick arches, the arch rings being faced in stone. The viaduct is on a slight curve in plan. Two of the arches carry the railway across the River Anker and there is a single skew arch over the B5000 road at the south end. The stone parapet wall overhangs the

129 *Stretton Aqueduct over the A5, carrying the Birmingham & Liverpool Junction Canal.*

side of the viaduct above a decorative stone moulding with ogee brackets. Four of the arches have tie bars through the arch, as does the river pier, and the three river piers have thickened bases. The original Engineer for the line was George Stephenson but when construction commenced he relinquished the post in favour of his son Robert. The viaduct cost £17,625 out of a total cost for the whole line of £830,000. The resident engineer was John Cass Birkinshaw, brought in to supervise the building of the railway from the London & Birmingham Railway, then also under construction. Following the completion of the line he became its Engineer and General Manager before moving on to other railway projects. The *Midland Counties Railway Hand-*

130 *River spans of the Anker Viaduct carrying the Birmingham & Derby Junction Railway.*

book (1840) describes the viaduct as 'scarcely surpassed for size and beauty' and it still remains an imposing structure. (HEW 886)

WOMBOURNE

ST31. Bratch Locks (SO 867939) Just north-west of Wombourne the Staffordshire & Worcestershire Canal descends 31ft 2in following the valley of the Smestow Brook by way of three locks at The Bratch. The locks were designed by James Brindley and opened to traffic on 1 April 1771. Originally the locks were built as a staircase of three with single deep gates separating the lock chambers. Later the locks were converted to the present arrangement of three separate locks by the addition of top gates to the two lowest locks.

The length of waterway between the separate locks thus formed is only about 15ft and such a short length could not accommodate the water discharged from the lock above without overflowing. Consequently long side ponds were constructed along the hillside on the west side of the locks connected by culverts through the canal walls. The lock chambers show evidence of the alterations, the stonework of bridge 48 being cut to allow the new top gate of the middle lock to open fully and the chamber walls of the lower two locks being recessed for the new gates. There is a neat octagonal toll house at the top of the locks. Under the bridge at the bottom of the locks is an unusually complex set of stairways in brickwork. (HEW 982)

131 *Bratch Locks at Staffs. & Worcs. Canal.*

ST32. Bratch Pumping Station (SO 869938), an important Victorian water pumping station situated just to the east of Bratch Locks, was built between 1895 and 1897 to pump drinking water from a deep underground source and raise it through a height of 350ft to a reservoir in Wolverhampton four miles away. It was built for Bilston Corporation. The pumps were powered by two large vertical triple expansion steam engines, each weighing 404 tons and about 40ft high named 'Alexandra' and 'Victoria'. The castings for the engines were produced by James Watt & Company but they were completed and erected by Thornewill & Wareham of Burton upon Trent. The high-pressure cylinder has a diameter of 16in, the intermediate pressure cylinder is 26in diameter and the low-pressure cylinder is 40in with a stroke of three feet. The engines are fitted with Corliss trip valves. Each engine has a flywheel 13ft 9in diameter and weighing 7¼ tons at each end of its crankshaft. The engines drove pumps sited below them and each engine was capable of supplying one million gallons of water in a 20-hour period. The engines worked until 1960 when they were replaced by electric pumps housed in a new building nearby, but between 1991 and 1996 the Victoria engine was reconstructed and repaired through the efforts of Mr Len Crane and the Friends of The Bratch. It has been steamed twice a year since 1997. The machinery and the ornate red brick building housing the engines was designed by Mr Baldwin Latham MICE of Westminster and its decorative brickwork and architectural detailing reflects the care taken over the appearance of utilitarian buildings in the Victorian age. The steam for the engines was originally provided by two Lancashire boilers, but these have been removed and the steam is now provided by an auxiliary oil-fired boiler. The old boiler house has been converted for use as a meeting room and reception area for visiting parties. The pumping station is not normally open to the public but public steaming days are held twice a year and it can be viewed by parties at other times by arrangement. See www.thebratch.org for details of openings.

132 *Bratch Water Pumping Station.*

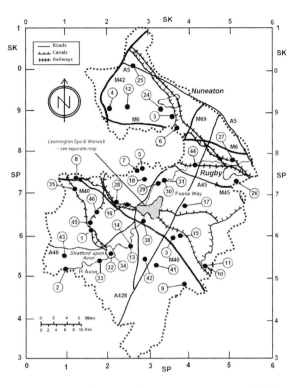

Map of Warwickshire (WK).

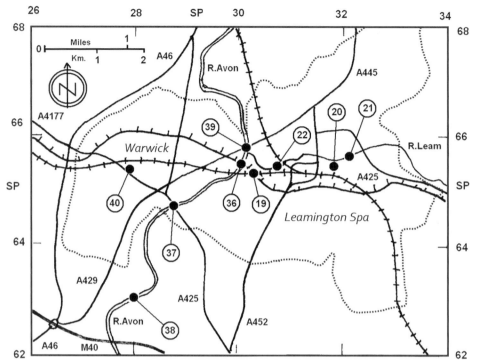

Map of Warwick and Leamington Spa.

BEARLEY

WK1. Bearley (Edstone) Aqueduct (SP 162609). Where the Stratford-upon-Avon Canal crosses the valley of a tributary of the River Alne east of Bearley, William Whitmore designed and built the longest cast-iron aqueduct in England, the second longest in Britain. The canal was built in three distinct stages, starting from its junc-

tion with the Worcester & Birmingham Canal at Kings Norton. It reached Hockley Heath in 1796, following which work on the canal stopped until 1799 when work restarted. By 1802 the canal had reached Kingswood, where it made a junction with the Warwick & Birmingham Canal. No further progress was made until 1812, when cutting began south of Kingswood under the direction of William Whitmore. Bearley Aqueduct has 14 spans of about 34ft and the waterway is carried in a cast-iron trough supported on brick piers. Cast-iron beams provide additional support under the trough, which is 498ft long overall. The trough sides and base are made up from flanged cast-iron plates bolted together. The base plate is extended on the east side to provide a towpath with a handrail. The setting of the towpath level with the base of the trough is reminiscent of Thomas Telford's aqueduct at Longdon upon Tern of 1795 (see above) and does not exhibit Telford's later design for Pontcysyllte (1805) where the towpath was set level with the top of the trough and

133 *Bearley or Edstone Aqueduct, Stratford-upon-Avon Canal.*

134 *Bidford Bridge, River Avon.*

cantilevered over the waterway to increase the effective hydraulic width of the canal. The design for Bearley could thus be considered somewhat old fashioned. In 1909 the Birmingham & North Warwickshire Railway was opened which passes under the aqueduct, and for a time water was supplied to the railway locomotives by a pipe from the aqueduct. (HEW 281)

BIDFORD ON AVON

WK 2. Bidford Bridge (SP 099518) is a late medieval bridge dating from the 15th century which shows the effects of much rebuilding. It has eight main arches and one flood arch and carries the B4085 road over the River Avon just south of the village. The arches have various spans and forms having been rebuilt over a long period of time. From the north the first two spans are pointed arches of irregular form, span 3 is segmental, 4 is semi-circular, arches 5, 6 and 7 are segmental and span 8 is pointed. The navigation arch is span 6. The spans of the arches are generally small, varying from 5ft 7in to 8ft 1in. The seven triangular cutwaters on the upstream face of the bridge are extended upwards to form pedestrian refuges, particularly necessary as the bridge is narrow and there is no footway. The bridge can be conveniently viewed from the adjacent river-side car park. (HEW 1021)

CHESTERTON

WK 3. Chesterton Windmill (SP 348594), which dates from 1632, is a tower mill of unconventional design constructed in limestone masonry. It is possible that Inigo Jones had a hand in its design; although there is no firm evidence for this he was a friend of

Sir Edward Peyto at whose instigation the mill was built and who may also have been involved in the design. It is also possible that the design was the work of John Webb, a pupil of Inigo Jones. The base of the mill, which is circular in plan with a diameter of 22ft 9in, has six semi-circular arches supported on rectangular piers. Fifteen feet above ground level is the first floor of the mill housing the mill stones and surmounted by a rotating domed timber cap containing the four common sails which have a span of 60ft. The machinery of the mill is of considerable interest. There are two pairs of stones driven from a vertical shaft which in turn is driven by an eight-foot-diameter brakewheel mounted on the windshaft holding the sails. The cap of the mill rotates on rollers which run in a cast-iron angle

135 *Chesterton Windmill.*

track screwed to an oak curb. The cap is rotated by means of a hand-operated winch with worm and spur gears. The final drive pinion of the winch engages with an 18ft-diameter oak rack gear on the wall of the tower. The mill has been repaired several times, with major repairs possibly being carried out in 1776 and 1860. In 1965 the mill was extensively restored by Warwickshire County Council in whose care the mill now resides. The mill, which stands in the centre of a field, can be viewed from the path running across the field. The mill is occasionally open to the public via a temporary staircase which gives access to the mill and its machinery. (HEW 867)

136 *Coleshill Bridge, west elevation.*

COLESHILL

WK 4. Coleshill Bridge (SP 199895) over the River Cole is a classic example of the widening of an ancient bridge in a contrasting material to accommodate modern traffic. The original bridge, which forms the east elevation of the present-day bridge, is in yellow sandstone with six segmental arches, their spans varying from 12ft 9in to 13ft 3in. It was built in the 15th or 16th century and was only 12ft 9in wide. All the stone piers have cutwaters in sandstone with the exception of the central cutwater which has (presumably) been rebuilt in red brick. Three of the cutwaters are extended upwards to form pedestrian refuges. In 1900 the bridge was widened to a total width of 18ft by building a matching extension of the existing arches on the west side, this time in red brick. Although the spans of the new arches are the same as the old ones, the radii of the new segmental arches is greater than the radii of the old arches, with the springing level of the new arches being raised to accommodate this. As there are no footways on the bridge a modern concrete footbridge has been sited parallel to it on the west side. To the north of the river bridge are three segmental brick flood arches.

COVENTRY

WK 5. Burton Green Water Tower (SP 268753), situated only a short distance from Tile Hill Water Tower (see below), was built about 1933. It is a reinforced concrete structure with a circular drum of 20,000 gallons' capacity on four reinforced concrete columns. It was erected to serve the Burton Green area but is now out of use. It is not accessible but can be viewed from the road nearby.

WK 6. Hawkesbury Junction Footbridge (SP 363846) An excellent example of a cast-iron arch towpath bridge, a larger version of many examples to be found on the Midlands canal network. The bridge which carries the towpath of the Coventry Canal over the entrance to the Oxford Canal at Hawkesbury junction is larger than usual, with a span of 60ft. It was erected in 1837 and is the work of John Sinclair, the Engineer to the Coventry Canal Company for many years. The ironwork for the bridge was cast at the Britannia Foundry in Derby by Handysides. The arch is formed from two ribs which also incorporate the bridge's handrails. Each rib is cast in two sections with a joint at the crown of the arch. (HEW 1111)

WK 7. Tile Hill Water Tower (SP 272763). This large prominent tower is situated in Cromwell Lane, Tile Hill, and was erected in 1932. It is a reinforced concrete tower

137 *Hawkesbury Junction Canal Bridge.*

138 *Earlswood Lakes Reservoir*

139 *Tile Hill Water Tower.*

with a capacity of 300,000 gallons. The tank is supported by a central shaft and prominent reinforced concrete ribs. It functioned as a balancing tank on the water supply to Meriden district but was taken out of use recently. It is not accessible but can be seen from the road nearby.

EARLSWOOD

WK 8. Earlswood Lakes reservoir (SP 113742) is an unusual arrangement of three pools to form a canal feeder reservoir, designed and built by Thomas Baylis for the Stratford-upon-Avon Canal in 1822, and is fed from the Spring Brook and its tributaries. The three pools are namely Windmill Pool (27 acres), Engine Pool (27 acres) and Terry's Pool (17 acres). The total amount of water retained is approximately 210 million gallons, equivalent to 14,000 locks of water. Windmill and Engine Pools are retained by an earth dam 1,400ft long and a maximum of 20ft high. A road runs along the top of the embankment and also along its foot. Terry's Pool is retained by a low earth embankment which runs along its southeast and south-west sides. A causeway with a road separates Windmill and Engine Pools and contains a common spillway (built 1986-7) which discharges overflow water from the pools into a vertical shaft and culvert running beneath the centre of the dam to emerge on the north side of the valley. Water from Terry's Pool overflows into Engine Pool. A feeder canal runs from the north-west end of the dam to the main line of the canal, about 600 yards to the north. The top water level in the reservoir is only a few inches above the normal water level in the canal and hence most of the water is supplied to the canal from the reservoir by pumping. The red brick building at the north-east end of the dam housed a steam-powered beam pumping engine installed in 1823, which worked until 1936 when it was replaced by electric pumps. (HEW 1654)

EDGE HILL

WK 9. Edge Hill Water Tower (SP 382483) is a 45ft-high reinforced concrete water tower prominently visible on the crest of Edge Hill. It has a circular tank 49ft in diameter with two compartments supported by a central shaft and 12 columns. The capacity of the tank is 180,000 gallons. The base of the tower houses a chamber with a remote level recorder. It supplies the parishes of Avon Dassett and Southam.

FENNY COMPTON

WK 10. Fenny Compton 'tunnel' (SP 433525 to SP 442520). During the construction of the Oxford Canal from Rugby to Banbury it was decided to drive a shallow tunnel though high ground to the east of Fenny Compton on the summit level of the canal. The tunnel was 1,138 yards long. In the 1830s the Oxford Canal Company decided to open out the tunnel in stages and purchased the land over the tunnel from Christ Church, Oxford, in 1838 at a cost of £591. The first stage of opening was between 1838 and 1840. In this stage 80 yards at the northern end, 155 yards in the centre and 115 yards at the south end were opened out. This left two short tunnels 336 and 452 yards long. The central open section was widened to allow boats to pass. The contractors for this stage were J. & W. Morgan, and barrow runs were used to haul the material out of the cutting. The cost was £3,964. In 1866-9 came the second phase of opening when the two short tunnels were removed. The Engineer for this work was Richard Gillett and the contractor was William Death; total cost was £15,000. Much of the clay excavated from the second opening was stored on the north side of the cutting and a brick works was established there to make bricks both for the use of the Canal Company and also for sale. During the opening out a number of structures were constructed spanning the cutting. They were bridge No. 137 – a brick arch accommodation bridge; bridge No. 138, carrying the Banbury turnpike road (rebuilt in the 1970s); bridge No. 139, a rectangular wrought-iron trough carrying the stream from the south to feed Wormleighton Canal reservoir. This trough has now been removed and the stream discharges directly into the canal. At a later date a small cast-iron roving bridge, No. 137A, was built. For details of this bridge see below. (HEW 38)

140 *(Above left) Edge Hill Water Tower.*

141 *(Above) Fenny Compton 'tunnel', Oxford Canal.*

142 *Oxford Canal bridge No. 137A.*

WK 11. Oxford Canal towpath bridge No. 137A (SP 433524). Following the opening out of Fenny Compton Tunnel (see above), a cast-iron arch bridge was constructed about halfway along the resulting cutting to transfer the towpath from one side of the canal to the other. The bridge is of conventional form with a semi-elliptical arch

143 *Furnace End Bridge's ribbed arch.*

of 26ft 9in span formed from two arch ribs, each cast in two sections with a central joint, which also form the handrail of the bridge. The deck is formed from cast-iron plates with a central rib and flanges to retain the gravel filling of the footway. The bridge may be viewed from the adjacent road bridge, No. 138, from where a path leads down to the towpath for a closer inspection. (HEW 1817)

FURNACE END

WK 12. Furnace End Bridge (SP 248913) is one of a small number of bridges in the county with a ribbed arch. It stands over the River Bourne just south of the crossroads in Furnace End and carries the B4114 road. The single arch, with a span of about 12ft, is medieval but unfortunately the bridge has been widened on the east side to nearly three times its original width and it is now nearly impossible to see the original arch which is on the west side of the bridge. Another bridge in the county with a ribbed arch is to be found at Stoneleigh (see below).

HAMPTON LUCY

WK 13. Charlecote Water Mill (SP 258572) is sited alongside the River Avon just to the north of Hampton Lucy village and is one of only a few water mills still in operation. It is a red brick three-storey building and was probably built in the 18th century but is on the site of earlier mills. Two mills at Hampton Lucy are recorded as belonging to the manor in Domesday Book of 1086. The mill is powered by two undershot water wheels fed by a leat from a weir on the River Avon. The west wheel has 42 paddles and is about 18ft diameter as is the east wheel which has 54 paddles. The wheels are cast iron with timber paddles, the wheel centre being cast in two pieces and centred with wedges. The name Ball & Horton, Millwrights, is cast on the hub of the west wheel. Power is taken from the wheels by vertical pit wheels geared to horizontal wallower wheels, which in turn are mounted on vertical timber shafts of octagonal section. The west wheel drives the two pairs of stones; the east wheel drives the ancillary machinery of the mill including the sack hoists. From the mill the water passes down a channel to rejoin the river about 250 yards downstream of the mill. The mill is in private ownership. (HEW 1978)

144 *Charlecote Water Mill.*

WK 14. Hampton Lucy Bridge (SP 258572), which replaced a ford and wooden causeway for pedestrians, is one of the few iron bridges in Warwickshire. It is sited where the road from Hampton Lucy to Charlecote crosses the River Avon. Here the Reverend John Lucy, vicar of Hampton Lucy, built, at his own expense, a cast-iron arch bridge with a single span of 60ft. There are four arch ribs, each made from four segments bolted together. The abutments of the bridge are unusual, being of well-worn sandstone ashlar masonry pierced with five narrow pointed arches, the arches increasing in height to match the rising level of the roadway as it approaches the bridge. The interior of the piers and arches of the abutment is in red brickwork. The ironwork was cast by Horseley Ironworks in 1829 and the designer may have been William Mackenzie, as a drawing of the bridge is in the Mackenzie papers at the Institution of Civil Engineers and at the time Mackenzie was working as Thomas Telford's resident engineer on the improvements to the Birmingham Canal. The contractor was Thomas Townshend. (HEW 1050)

145 *Hampton Lucy Bridge.*

HARBURY

WK 15. Harbury Windmill (SP 373600), with a height of about 60ft, was the tallest tower mill in Warwickshire. It was built about 1805 and has a brick tower with, originally, a boat-shaped cap containing four common sails. In order for the miller to reach the sails to furl or unfurl their canvas covering, a gallery was provided running round the mill, only the stumps of which now remain. The mill had three pairs of stones and was worked by wind power until the early years of the 20th century when the sails were removed following which it was worked by a steam engine and later electrical power. The tower has now been converted into a house and the original cap replaced by a new square cap with a pitched roof. It is not accessible but may be viewed from the roads in the village.

146 *Harbury Windmill.*

HATTON

WK 16. Hatton Locks (SP 264655 to SP 241669) is one of the greatest lock flights in Britain, exceeded in this region only by the flight of 30 locks at Tardebigge in Worcestershire (see below). At Hatton the Warwick & Birmingham Canal descends nearly 147ft into the valley of the River Avon. To overcome this descent the company built a flight of 21 locks, the fall of each lock therefore being seven feet. The flight extends over a distance of 3,400 yards, the spacing of the locks varying with the slope of the ground, the spacing increasing towards the bottom of the flight as the ground flattens out. The original locks were 'narrow', for boats 70ft long and seven feet wide. These locks opened in 1799 and the Engineers were William Felkin (until 1796) followed by Charles Handley. Subsequently the Warwick & Birmingham Canal became part of the Grand Union Canal network and in 1932-4 the locks were completely rebuilt as part of the scheme to widen the canal for 14ft-wide boats from London to Birmingham. The new locks have chambers 90ft long and 15ft 4in wide with double mitred gates at

147 *Hatton Locks – new lock and old lock chamber.*

both ends. The paddle gear is enclosed, an indicator rod being provided to show the position of the paddle. In the majority of cases the old lock chambers were retained to act as overflow weirs for the new locks. Where the old chamber is on the towpath side they have been decked over in concrete. (HEW 1037)

HUNNINGHAM

WK 17. Hunningham Railway Bridge (SP 383665) was for a short time the longest lattice girder bridge in the world. In 1850 the London & North Western Railway was constructing its line from Leamington Spa to Rugby. South of Hunningham the line passes through a deep cutting and across a trackway from Harbury to Hunningham. To accommodate the road an interesting large wrought-iron lattice girder bridge was built that originally spanned 150ft across the complete width of the cutting. The girders are 10ft 6in deep and the roadway is sited at about the mid-depth of the girders. The bridge is about 50ft above the railway. The designer of the bridge was William Thomas Doyne, the resident engineer for the construction of the railway. Doyne gave a paper on the design of the bridge at an Institution of Civil Engineers meeting in 1850. Subsequently the bridge has been propped at its third points by a complex arrangement of four lattice columns, cross-braced by tie rods, thus converting it into a three-span bridge. The bridge is best viewed from the 'Greenway' footpath which now follows the old railway track. (HEW 2044)

148 *Tainters Hill Water Tower house conversion.*

KENILWORTH

WK 18. Tainters Hill Windmill/Water Tower (SP 290728), now a house, was built in 1778 as a tower windmill. In 1854 the mill was converted to steam power and in 1884 was

further converted into a water tower by placing a 26,000-gallon iron tank on the top of the windmill tower. In 1925 the tank was replaced by a larger one of 50,000 gallons but this became derelict in the 1960s and in 1974 the tower was converted into a dwelling by architect E.R. Byron. The tower is private property but can be seen from the nearby roads.

LEAMINGTON SPA

WK 19. Leamington Canal Aqueduct (SP 303653) was inserted under an existing canal by the Great Western Railway on its line from Leamington to Birmingham. It is sited where the railway crosses the line of the Warwick & Napton Canal a short distance from the canal's crossing of the River Avon (see below). To accommodate the canal the railway company built an unusual aqueduct over the line. The waterway is carried in a cast-iron trough which is supported by six cast-iron arches of slightly unorthodox design. The arch ribs are cast as double cantilevers resting on the brick piers but do not extend for the full span. The ribs engage with lugs cast on the bottom of the trough so that the trough itself acts as the centre of the arch. The towpath is carried on external brick

149 *Leamington Spa Canal Aqueduct over the railway.*

arches which partly conceal the ironwork behind. The contractors for the aqueduct were Peto and Betts and it was completed in 1852. The aqueduct can be viewed from the towpath of the canal accessed from the canal bridge on Myton Road but the ironwork is not visible. (HEW 495)

WK 20. Leamington Spa swimming pool roof (SP 318655) is an interesting roof design in cast and wrought iron. In 1890 the pool was constructed at the rear of the Pump Room in Leamington Spa. To cover the pool the then borough engineer, William de Normanville, designed an iron and timber roof 120ft long with a span of 60ft. The roof consists of a central pitched area 60ft long with a hipped roof at the east end and a five-sided apse at the west end. The roof is slated and there is a raised clerestory along the ridge. The roof is supported by timber purlins and rafters with iron trusses. The trusses are made up from cast-iron compression members of cruciform section and wrought-iron tie rods forming the tension members. To balance the outward thrust of the ends of the roof there are two tensioned tie rods 2in in diameter running the length of the central section of the roof, each rod tensioned by a turnbuckle at its centre. There are complex castings where the end trusses meet at the apex of the roof, especially at the west end. In the late 1980s the building was under threat of demolition as part of the redevelopment of the Pump Room site but the building has now been restored and, although no longer in use as a swimming pool, is now a public library. (HEW 1742)

150 *Leamington Spa swimming pool roof (now a public library).*

WK 21. Mill Road Suspension Bridge (SP 321656). In order to carry a footpath from Mill Road into Jepson Gardens an unusual suspension bridge was designed by the borough engineer, William de Normanville. Instead of the usual suspension chains, the 100ft-span bridge is supported by wrought-iron rods running diagonally from the tops of the two towers to vertical hangers at the top of the handrail on the third points of the span. Three rods run from each tower on each side of the bridge, two to the nearer third point and one to the further third point. On the landward side of the towers the three rods run down to an anchorage. The deck is supported on each side by lattice girders with cross beams. In some ways the form of the bridge anticipates the modern cable-stayed suspension bridge. Underneath the bridge the river falls over a curved, stepped weir with the gardens forming a pleasing background. The name Mill Road originates from Oldham's Mill which stood on the site until it was demolished in 1889. (HEW 1585)

WK 22. Princes Drive Bridge (SP 309655) is a reinforced concrete bridge which carries Princes Drive over the River Leam. It was opened on 14 June 1923 to a design by the Trussed Steel Concrete Company with A. Jackman & Co. Ltd of Slough as contractors. Most early reinforced concrete bridges were the work of L.G. Mouchel using the Hennebique system. Princes Drive Bridge is of particular interest as it was *not* designed by Mouchel.

There are three spans over the river with two flood spans to the north. The three main river spans are 39ft 5in with 10 beams across the width of the bridge. These are supported on six reinforced concrete columns, the tops of which are connected by a transverse beam. The spacing of the beams is not symmetrical, the nine beams from the east face of the bridge being spaced three feet apart while the 10th beam is spaced 7ft 1in from its neighbour. This beam is also shallower than the others, being 17in deep compared with 29in deep. For this reason vehicles are prevented from encroaching on the footway on the west side of the bridge. There has been some attempt to improve the appearance of the bridge with decorative detail at the tops of the piers and on the parapet walls, which are terminated by large concrete blocks. There are ornate lamp columns set on the parapet blocks although these have now been superseded by modern steel lamp columns. (HEW 2350)

151 Princes Drive Bridge, Leamington Spa.

NUNEATON
WK 23. Arbury Hall Canals (SP 366883 to SP 329905) is a network of private canals unique in the region and built in the grounds of Arbury Hall near Nuneaton by Sir Roger Newdigate for carrying coal and other goods around the estate. The canals were also used for pleasure boating. The network was constructed over a number of years and in some cases many years elapsed between the commencement of work and the final completion of the canal. There was a connection via the 1,078-yard Coventry Communication Canal to the nearby Coventry Canal. Seven separate canals can be identified together with the separate Griff Hollows Canal, built 1785-7 and 1,320 yards long, which linked the Coventry Canal to Griff Wharf. The other canals in the network were:

Arbury Lower Level Canal, 1,100 yards with six locks, built 1770-3;
Coventry Wood Canal, 528 yards with two locks, built 1771-89;
Arbury Upper Canal, 2,508 yards with four locks including a 'triple' lock, built 1764-73;
Seeswood Canal, 1,980 yards with one lock, built 1778-84;
Coton Lawn Canal, 2,112 yards, built 1769-95;
The New Cut, 440 yards, built 1793.

There were 13 locks in total, plus a stop lock at the junction with the Coventry Canal and the whole system extended for 6¼ miles. The locks were 40ft long by six feet wide and the boats were approximately 35ft long and six-foot beam. The triple lock on the Arbury Upper canal was Y-shaped with two sets of gates at its upper end, a most unusual, if not unique, feature. It is not known who built the canals, but William Bean and John Morris worked on the locks on the Arbury Upper Canal. At the upper end the canals were fed from a reservoir at Seeswood Pool (see below) situated 93ft 6in above the lowest level of the system. Following the death of Sir Roger Newdigate in 1806 the canal system fell into disuse and most had been abandoned by 1819 with the exception of the Coventry Communication Canal and the Griff Hollows Canal, which was in use until 1961. Traces of some of the canals can still be seen but the grounds of Arbury Hall are private, only open to the public from time to time. (HEW 217)

WK 24. Seeswood Reservoir (SP 329905). Built in 1764, Seeswood Pool, as it is now known, is considered to be the earliest canal feeder reservoir in Britain. It was built to supply water to the privately owned Arbury Hall canal system (see above). The reservoir was created from an existing natural lake by building an earth dam about 460ft long and 33ft wide at the top, along which runs the B4102 road from Nuneaton to Meriden. The maximum height of the dam is about 22ft. Originally the reservoir discharged water into a feeder channel leading to the Arbury canals but in 1777 the feeder was made navigable as the Seeswood Canal. Most unusually, in 1784 a lock was constructed through the dam at the south end to allow boats to pass from the canal into the reservoir. At some time after the abandonment of the canal system the north-east side of the lock chamber was partially demolished and the resulting slope concreted over to form a spillway; the

152 *Dam and site of lock at Seeswood Pool.*

original entrance from the lock into the reservoir was blocked with a brick wall. The reservoir is now used for fishing. It may be viewed from the B4102 road. (HEW 1730)

POLESWORTH

WK 25. Polesworth Bridge (SK 261023) has 10 arches and carries a road over the River Anker in Polesworth village. The west side of the bridge is the original structure, built in 1776 in red brick with stone arch rings. All the arches are semi-circular and have spans varying from 15ft 8in to 20ft 9in. The parapet contains a stone inscribed 'HL 1776 TS'. The HL almost certainly refers to Henry Lakin and TS refers to Thomas Sheasby senior, then a local builder from Tamworth who designed and built the bridge for £364 and later became a substantial canal engineer and contractor. The bridge was only 16ft wide and in 1924 it was widened on its east side by a further 22ft 2in in mass concrete. The new arches were cast directly against the old arches and exactly match the spans. The bridge is a scheduled Ancient Monument.

RUGBY

WK 26. Ashlawn Water Tower (SP 507729), built in 1934, is a prominent landmark on the ridge to the south of Rugby. It is a circular reinforced concrete tower with a 500,000-gallon tank supported on 12 reinforced concrete columns.

WK 27. Cosford Aqueduct (SP 503771). In the 1830s extensive improvements were carried out to the line of the Oxford Canal between Coventry and Rugby. In particular the line was shortened considerably by cutting off the meandering loops characteristic of this canal. Cosford Aqueduct was built on one of these new lengths to carry the canal over a minor road north-west of the town centre and dates from about 1834. The Engineers for the improvements to the canal were William Cubitt and Frederick Wood, with the ironwork for the aqueduct being supplied by Parkes & Ottway. The waterway is carried in a trough 15ft wide which spans 23ft 6in between the abutments. The iron trough is built up from base and side plates with bolted joints. The trough was originally supported by four cast-iron segmental arch ribs with a higher segmental

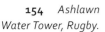

153 *Polesworth Bridge, west elevation.*

154 *Ashlawn Water Tower, Rugby.*

155 *Cosford Aqueduct, Oxford Canal.*

cast-iron arch on both sides that supported the towpath. By 1988 three of the four ribs had been fractured by collisions with over-height vehicles and were replaced by steel joists. However in 1991 the aqueduct was extensively repaired, the four arch ribs were replaced by new cast-iron ribs and the whole structure repainted. The road underneath the aqueduct is now closed to all traffic to safeguard the structure from further damage. (HEW 1720)

SHREWLEY

WK 28. Shrewley Canal Tunnel (SP 214673) is distinctive in that at the west end the towpath, after rising from the side of the deep cutting leading to the canal tunnel, passes through a short tunnel of its own high above the canal before emerging to reach the village of Shrewley. The canal tunnel itself is not of any great distinction, being 433 yards long, brick-lined with no towpath. The towpath tunnel is about 175ft long, on a steeply rising gradient. The width of the tunnel varies from 9ft 6in at its lower end to 8ft 4in at the upper end. Most of the tunnel is paved with brick with raised courses to afford a grip to the hooves of horses, but the highest 32ft of the tunnel has recent concrete steps. After crossing the village street the towpath follows the line of the tunnel to rejoin the canal at its eastern end. The canal and tunnel were completed in 1799. The towpath tunnel can be accessed down a narrow footpath between the houses on the west side of the main street. (HEW 707)

STONELEIGH

WK 29. Stare Bridge (SP 329714) is an ancient bridge, now preserved. Until 1929 the road from Coventry to Leamington Spa crossed the River Avon by way of it. There are references to a bridge at this site being in a state of disrepair in 1278 and 1352 but the present bridge may date from the 14th or 15th century. It is said to have been built by the monks of Stoneleigh Abbey and has nine arches of varying size and style. The five southernmost arches, the first three of which cross the river, are pointed arches to a

157 *Stare Bridge.* lesser or greater degree, the next two arches are segmental and the northernmost two arches are pointed. All the upstream piers have cut waters which extend upwards to form pedestrian refuges, probably necessary when the bridge was in use for traffic as the roadway is only about 10ft wide. In 1929 the road was diverted away to the east and a new bridge built over the river. A public footpath crosses the bridge.

WK 30. Stoneleigh Abbey (Grecian Lodge) Bridge (SP 317715). In 1813 an elegant stone bridge was completed across the River Avon on a private approach road to Stoneleigh Abbey to a design by John Rennie. The bridge has a single segmental masonry arch of 91ft span and two small side arches with semi-circular arches of 13ft span. The large arch voussoirs have deep V-joints. The bridge is generally constructed in a pale cream sandstone but the interior of the two side arches includes some red sandstone blocks. Documents in the records of the Stoneleigh Abbey Estate reveal that in a report dated September 1811, Humphry Repton, the landscape architect, reported consultations

158 *(Below) Grecian Lodge Bridge at Stoneleigh Abbey.* with John Rennie and Rennie's recommendation of an iron bridge. It must be presumed that at some time between 1811 and 1813 the design was changed to the present masonry arch. The bridge can be viewed by visitors to the park, which is open to the public at times. For opening times see www.stoneleighabbey.org. (HEW 2144)

WK 31. Stoneleigh Bridge (SP 332727). In Stoneleigh village the Coventry to Leamington Spa road crosses the River Sowe by way of a red sandstone masonry arch bridge with

159 *(Below right) Stoneleigh Bridge river arches.* eight segmental spans. The fifth arch from the north is ribbed with three rectangular ribs, one of only a small number of bridges in the county showing this feature. In 1844 the bridge was widened on the downstream side to the design of William Kendall,

County Surveyor, and this is apparent from the discontinuity of the arches when seen from underneath, the newer arches having a greater span. In 1971 a timber footway which rests on the piers of the old bridge was added on the upstream side of the bridge.

STRATFORD-UPON-AVON

WK 32. Clopton Bridge (SP 206548) is a historic bridge over the River Avon at Stratford-upon-Avon with an interesting cast-iron footway. A bridge at this site is first mentioned in 1235. By 1269 it was referred to as 'The Great Bridge' and was a timber structure with a chapel at the south end. The present stone bridge is named after its builder, Sir Hugh Clopton, who was Lord Mayor of London in 1492. The bridge dates from about 1485. It presently has 14 arches carrying the A34 road over the river. The original arches are part segmental with a slight point, the spans varying from 18ft 6in to 18ft and can best be seen from downstream of the bridge. In 1814 the bridge was widened on its upstream face by building new arches 5ft 3in wide on new piers, the new arches having increased spans of between 25ft 5in and 29ft 2in. The new and old arches can be clearly seen from upstream. Later, in 1827 a cast-iron footway 3ft 9in wide was added alongside the bridge on the upstream side. The footway is carried on cast-iron brackets cantilevered from the side of the bridge. Vertical brackets founded on the cutwaters of the bridge give additional support. A hexagonal toll house stands at the north-west corner of the bridge bearing the inscription 'Sir Hugh Clopton, Knight built this bridge in the reign of King Henry the Seventh'. (HEW 679)

160 *Clopton Bridge with cast-iron footway, Stratford-upon-Avon.*

WK 33. Stratford Railway Viaduct (SP 188533) is a good example of the reuse of a redundant railway bridge as part of a long-distance pedestrian and cycle route. The track of the Great Western Railway line south of Stratford-upon-Avon crossed the River Avon by means of a substantial steel girder bridge and masonry viaduct. The main bridge over the river has a skew span of 114ft and consists of three large riveted girders 131ft long with 11 panels. The outermost panels are triangular, the next three have N-bracing and the centre three panels have X-bracing. The girders are about 12ft high. The bridge deck is supported on transverse lattice beams with longitudinal beams which would have supported the rail tracks. On both sides of the main bridge there are four span brick arch

161 *Viaduct over River Avon.*

viaducts with 25ft-span segmental arches. The viaduct has an interesting history. In 1859 the Oxford, Worcester & Wolverhampton Railway opened a single-line standard-gauge branch to Stratford-upon-Avon from Honeybourne to the south. One year later the Great Western Railway opened a mixed-gauge branch line from the north to Stratford from Hatton. In 1861 the two branches were connected end to end following which trains ran between Leamington Spa and Worcester. In 1906, the GWR (now the owners of the OWWR) rebuilt and doubled the line from Stratford to Honeybourne as part of its scheme

for an independent line from Birmingham to Cheltenham. At that time the viaduct was built in its present form. (HEW 1830)

WK 34. Tramway Bridge (SP 205548) is the largest structure on the Stratford & Moreton tramway. The tramway, opened in 1826, crossed the River Avon immediately to the south of its wharves alongside the terminal basin of the Stratford-upon-Avon Canal and just downstream from Clopton Bridge (see above). The bridge was designed by the Engineer to the tramway company, John Urpeth Rastrick, and is in red brick with nine semi-elliptical arches of 30ft span. The contractor for the building of the bridge was George Roe, assisted by his son, John, and Richard Clark. The tramway was abandoned and the track lifted in 1918 but the bridge has survived and is now used as a pedestrian footway. (HEW 868)

162   Umberslade Hall Drive Bridge.

TANWORTH IN ARDEN
WK 35. Umberslade Hall Drive Bridge (SP 119709) is a superb example of late skew masonry arch bridge construction. It carries the line of the ex-Great Western Railway line from Tyseley to Stratford-upon-Avon (the North Warwickshire Railway) over the driveway leading from Tanworth in Arden to Umberslade Hall. A small stream flows through the eastern arch. The bridge has three spans on an acute skew angle, the arches being semi-elliptical in form and built in finely dressed ashlar sandstone. It will be noted that the first three courses of masonry in the arches are horizontal. Above this is a single course of blocks cut to twice the normal size and notched to receive the skew blocks comprising the remainder of the arch. The centre span is 39ft and the side spans 31ft on the skew. The bridge dates from about 1908, the railway having opened on 1 July of that year. The Engineer was H.D. Smith, the resident engineer for the GWR, and the contractor was C.J. Wills & Son. The bridge is built to a much higher standard than most of the other bridges on the line, presumably for the owners of Umberslade Hall.

163   Aqueduct carrying Warwick & Napton Canal over River Avon.

WARWICK
WK 36. Avon Aqueduct (SP 301655) The largest structure on the Warwick & Napton Canal (now part of the Grand Union system) where it crosses the River Avon just east of Warwick. The aqueduct has three masonry arch spans of 43ft span and carries the waterway about 30ft above the normal river level. The arch rings are in V-jointed ashlar masonry 2ft 6in thick, the remaining stonework being in plain sandstone ashlar. The towpath is on the north side of the aqueduct with a concrete parapet wall dated 1909 which has been cast directly onto the old stone coping. On the other side is a modern handrail erected in the 1980s. The aqueduct dates from about 1798 and was built by Benjamin Lloyd, Moses Wilson (masons) and John Docker and Thomas Wilson (carpenters).

The Engineer for the canal was William Felkin from 1794 until 1796 when he was replaced by Charles Handley, a local man from Barford. The aqueduct may be visited by walking along the towpath of the canal from nearby Emscote Road bridge. (HEW 641)

WK 37. Castle Bridge (SP 288647). In 1788 the Earl of Warwick obtained an Act to build a new bridge to replace the 'Great Bridge' which had been built near the Castle by 1208 with 13 arches. By 1373 it was largely in ruin and most of it was swept away in 1795. The proposed new bridge was part of a scheme to extend the Castle park to the east. The new bridge was built by William Eboral, a stonemason, following closely the design of Leafield Bridge (see below). The first stone was laid in 1789 and the new bridge was opened in 1793 at a cost of £3,258. It has a large single arch in ashlar masonry with a span of 105ft. The arch ring is 3ft 6in deep with banded ashlar blocks. The bridge is a scheduled Ancient Monument. From the bridge the remnants of the Great Bridge may be seen downstream. (HEW 1089)

164 *Castle Bridge, Warwick.*

WK 38. Leafield Bridge (SP 280630) is an earlier near-twin of Castle Bridge at Warwick (see above) and designed by Robert Mylne, an architect and civil engineer who designed many bridges including Blackfriars Bridge in London. It is a single-span masonry arch bridge of 102ft span completed in 1776. The arch ring is three feet thick in banded ashlar masonry similar to the Castle Bridge arch but the bridge is about one half the width. The bridge lies on private land and is not accessible to the public. (HEW 1088)

165 *(Below left) Leafield Bridge.*

WK 39. Portobello (Emscote) Bridge (SP 301658), carrying the road linking Warwick with Leamington Spa over the River Avon, has an interesting history of rebuilding. An ancient bridge existed just upstream of the present bridge but in the 1820s it was reported to be narrow, unsafe, ruinous and broken down. A contract was awarded to

166 *(Below) Porto-bello Bridge.*

167 *Warwick gasworks.*

Thomas Townshend for a bridge with two semi-elliptical arches of 60ft span. A temporary bridge was erected by Townshend while construction proceeded. The bridge was opened on 7 May 1832. Later, concern was expressed at the condition of the bridge, mainly due to the sinking of the crowns of the rather flat arches. In 1892 timber centering was placed under the arches by Francis Cheffin of Westminster at a cost of £1,030. In May 1892 tenders were invited for the complete rebuilding of the arches of the bridge with segmental arches in brick with stone facings. However, the bridge as it stands today suggests that the arches may not have been completely rebuilt as planned. The sections of the arches nearest the piers remain, in stone with a brick section in the middle of the arch, and there is a marked dissimilarity between the large pale stone blocks with the smaller, darker stones of the facing to the brick sections. The bridge has been widened on both sides to improve pedestrian access. On the north side an iron footway has been added with wrought-iron brackets cantilevered from the side of the arches with a walkway about five feet wide supported on iron plates. On the south side is a modern widening with steel columns founded on the cut water of the central stone pier and the false cutwaters at the abutments, which support steel I-beams and a concrete slab footway with a steel parapet rail. In 2008 proposals for substantial alterations of the bridge were publicised and it is possible that this form of the bridge will not match that given in this description. (HEW 2414)

WK 40. Warwick Gasworks (SP 278653). This white-painted building situated in Saltisford is the site of one of the earliest gasworks in the world. The original buildings were erected in 1822 and included two octagonal towers each containing a gas holder with other buildings to the rear, now demolished. Later, in about 1905, a single-storey office building was added between the towers. In more recent times extra storeys were added to the central section which remained in use for offices until about 2001. The coal for the gas production was delivered by canal boat to the nearby Saltisford Basin until the

168 *(Below right) Estate Drive Bridge, Compton Verney.*

169 *Wellesbourne Water Mill.*

building of the adjacent Oxford & Birmingham Railway (later GWR) when a siding into the gasworks was laid. The gas manufactured at the works was supplied to the town of Warwick and also in 1823 by way of a three-mile main to illuminate lamps in Union Parade in Leamington Spa. The gasworks site is private but the exterior of the buildings may be viewed from the A425 Saltisford Road.

WELLESBOURNE

WK 41. Compton Verney Estate Bridge (SP313529) has three segmental arches in ashlar masonry and carries the carriage drive leading to Compton Verney house over Compton Pool, an artificial lake. It was designed by Robert Adam and built in the later 18th century. It is a scheduled Ancient Monument.

WK 42. Wellesbourne Water Mill (SP 287537) is one of a few examples of a working water mill in the county. It is situated on the River Dene at Wellesbourne and is powered by a breast shot water wheel 17ft in diameter and 6ft wide that drives two sets of French millstones. The vertical drive shaft unusually has a crown wheel, connected via a bevel

170 *Wixford Bridge.*

gear to a horizontal shaft which passes through the wall of the mill and enables the stones to be driven by an external power source, either a steam engine or a tractor, in times of drought. The mill building is rectangular in red brick with a tiled roof. The date 1834 is picked out in blue brick on the north elevation. Immediately adjacent to the mill is the miller's house, a two-storey red brick building with dormer windows in the tiled roof. Next to the miller's house is the bake house, originally used for bread making but now a workshop and store. There are other buildings on the site including a large barn which has been used as a visitor centre. The water for the mill is

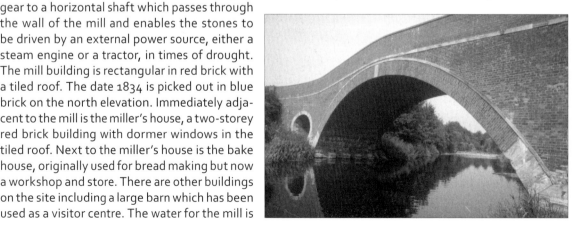

171 *Wolston Viaduct, London & Birmingham Railway.*

retained in a pond to the south of the mill by a dam with a spillway. Wellesbourne Mill is probably one of three mills listed in Domesday Book for Walton in 1086 which were owned by the Earl of Warwick. The earliest known miller was Alexander Bradford in 1638. It was rebuilt in 1834 for Sir John Mordaunt. The mill last worked by water power before 1939 but then continued in use with an external power source before eventually becoming disused. In 1988 the dam was repaired in concrete and the mill restored to use, flour production being resumed in 1989. The mill is not currently open to the public.

WIXFORD
WK 43. Wixford Bridge (SP 087546) is the finest brick bridge in the county and one of the finest in the region. It carries the B4085 road over the River Arrow just to the north of the village. The single red brick segmental arch spans 65ft over the river. The arch ring is in brickwork and is 30in thick except for the first few feet from the abutments which are in sandstone. The spandrel walls of the bridge are pierced by circular holes 8ft 4in in diameter lined internally with brick but with stone rings at the outer ends. The holes give access along the river bank and provide extra passage for water in time of flood. The designer of the bridge was Henry Couchman senior and it was completed in 1801. (HEW 1781)

172 *Wootton Wawen Aqueduct, Stratford-upon-Avon Canal.*

WOLSTON
WK 44. Wolston Viaduct (SP 409761) is an original structure on the London & Birmingham Railway across the River Avon between Rugby and Coventry. Robert Stephenson designed a low viaduct with nine main arches which features in one of the contemporary illustrations of the railway by John Bourne. The semi-elliptical arches which span 24ft are built in brick, the exterior of the arches and the sides of the viaduct being

173 *Yarningale Aqueduct, Stratford-upon-Avon Canal.*

faced in stone. At each end are three smaller semi-circular arches of 10ft span. Later work on the viaduct has consisted of the addition of tie bars and plates above the arches, two to each span, and the bricking up of two of the smaller arches at the west end of the viaduct to enable the embankment to be extended. Just to the west of the viaduct is the site of Brandon & Wolston station which closed in 1960. (HEW 767)

WOOTTON WAWEN
WK 45. Wootton Wawen Aqueduct (SP 159630) is the second largest of three similar aqueducts on the southern section of the Stratford-upon-Avon Canal. It carries the waterway across the A3400 road in a cast-iron trough made up of 12 sections with bolted joints. Three brick piers divide the aqueduct into four unequal spans with cast-iron beams supporting the trough. The details of the construction of the trough are identical to Bearley (Edstone) Aqueduct (see above). A plaque on the east side of the trough records that it was erected by the Stratford Canal Company in October 1813, Chairman Bernard Dewes Esq. and Deputy Chairman William James. The Engineer was William Whitmore. (HEW 282)

YARNINGALE
WK 46. Yarningale Aqueduct (SP 184664) is the smallest of the three aqueducts on the southern section of the Stratford-upon-Avon Canal. It is unusually situated immediately adjacent to the north end of a lock and crosses a small stream. Structurally it is identical to the larger aqueducts at Bearley and Wootton Wawen (see above). The ironwork was cast by the Horseley Company. The aqueduct dates from 1834, 21 years after the opening of the canal as it is not the first aqueduct at this site, the original structure having been destroyed by a flood generated by a burst on the nearby Warwick & Birmingham Canal. (HEW 655)

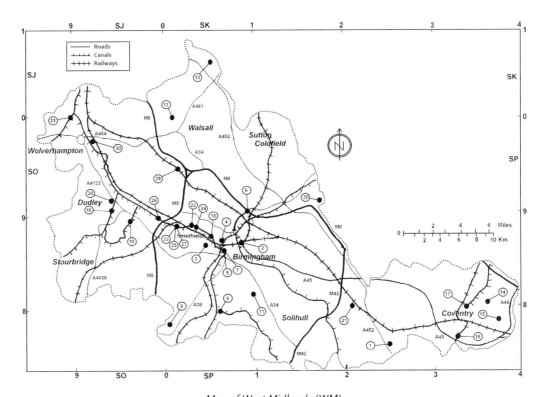

Map of West Midlands (WM).
Note that some canals and railways have been omitted for clarity (see Chapters 2 and 3).

WM 1. Berkswell Windmill
WM 2. Curzon Street station, Birmingham
WM 3. Edgbaston Reservoir
WM 4. Farmers Bridge Locks
WM 5. Gas Street Basin
WM 6. Gravelly Hill Interchange
WM 7. Holliday Street Aqueduct
WM 8. Hollymoor Hospital Water Tower
WM 9. Kings Norton stop lock
WM 10. Lee Bridge & Winson Green Bridge
WM 11. Sarehole Mill, Birmingham
WM 12. Birchills Aqueduct
WM 13. Brownhills Aqueduct
WM 14. Alpha House, Coventry
WM 15. Binley Road Bridge, Coventry
WM 16. Coat of Arms Bridge, Coventry

WM 17. Coventry Canal Basin
WM 18. Dudley Canal Tunnel
WM 19. Netherton Tunnel, Dudley
WM 20. Tipton Lift Bridge
WM 21. Hampton in Arden packhorse Bridge
WM 22. Engine Arm Aqueduct, Smethwick
WM 23. Galton Bridge
WM 24. Rabone Lane Canal Junction Bridges
WM 25. Smethwick Cutting
WM 26. Spon Lane Lock Flight
WM 27. Steward Aqueduct, Smethwick
WM 28. Water Orton Bridge
WM 29. Taylor's Aqueduct, W. Bromwich
WM 30. Chillington Wharf, Wolverhampton
WM 31. Tunstall (Dunstall) Water Bridge

BERKSWELL

WM1. Berkswell Windmill (SP 249759) is a unique tower windmill situated appropriately on Windmill Lane at Balsall Common. The mill stands on a low mound surrounded by a circular wall, the only complete one of its type in the British Isles. The red brick tower has three storeys and a boat-shaped cap. There are four sails, two common sails and two patent sails spanning 60ft. It has two pairs of millstones. It was built in 1826 to replace a former post mill and was worked by the Hammond family for over 100 years. In 1927 wind working ceased after which it was worked by an oil engine until 1948. The sails were removed in 1932. Following a change of ownership the mill was restored in 1973-5 when a new cap and four new sails were fitted. Normally the windmill is open to the public on some weekends but at the time of writing the mill is undergoing a further extensive restoration and is currently not open to the public. There is an admission charge.

174   Berkswell Windmill.

BIRMINGHAM

WM 2. Curzon Street station (SP 087871). The original terminal building of the London & Birmingham Railway is one of the few surviving structures from the line which opened in 1838. The building was designed by Philip Hardwick and built by contractors Grissel and Peto. Architecturally it is a square building of ashlar masonry in three storeys with four giant Ionic columns forming the portico. The choice of the Ionic style was presumably a deliberate choice to contrast with the Doric portico at the other end of the line at Euston. The interior of the building contained the booking hall with a steep iron balustraded stone staircase, a refreshment room, directors' rooms, secretaries and engineers offices. The survival of the building was due to the opening, in 1852, of New Street station to which all passenger services were transferred. Curzon Street continued to handle excursion trains until 1893 after which it became a goods station only. Originally it was flanked by the *Queens Hotel* on its north side but this was demolished in the 1960s. The building has been renovated and restored for alternative uses while retaining its original outward appearance and for a time was in use as the headquarters of the Prince's Trust. The building is in private ownership and is not open to the public, but the exterior may be viewed from the nearby streets. (HEW 420)

175   Curzon Street station, London & Birmingham Railway.

WM 3. Edgbaston Reservoir (SP 043867) is a canal reservoir, originally known as Rotton Park Reservoir, built in 1825-8 as an important part of the improvements to the main line of the Birmingham Canal under the direction of Thomas

Telford. The water is retained by a large dam of earth construction with a puddled clay core and is about 1,140ft long. There is an overflow weir at the south end of the dam which discharges into the Icknield Port Loop of the canal. The dam is described in various references as being between 41 and 43 feet high but in May 1828 before the reservoir was completed Telford suggested an increase in height of four feet which was agreed by the Committee of the Birmingham Canal Company. As completed the dam is 45ft high, the depth of water behind the dam being 42ft. The inner slope of the dam is brick-faced, the outer slope grassed. The water is discharged from the reservoir into the canal by means of two discharge valves sited on the inner face of the dam then through an 18in-diameter pipe passing through the dam. The reservoir is unusual in that the majority of water flowing into it comes from higher levels of the Birmingham Canal Navigations (BCN), in particular the Titford level, a complex water management system ensuring maximum use of the water supply. The 62½ acres of the reservoir contains enough water to fill 15,650 locks. The reservoir and the surrounding area is open to the public. (HEW 1584)

WM 4. Farmers Bridge Locks (SP 061870 to SP 072877) is of major significance in the history of the BCN. The flight of 13 narrow locks in the centre of Birmingham marks the

commencement of the Birmingham & Fazeley Canal and carries the canal from its junction with the Birmingham Canal down a vertical height of 90ft over a distance of about a thousand yards. The lock chambers have single top and bottom gates each with two ground paddles. With the exception of the bottom lock (No. 13), all the locks are provided with short lengths of waterway alongside the lock chamber with an overflow at the end. These lengths provide an increased volume of water in the relatively short pounds between the locks as well as loading and unloading area for the boats that served the factories originally lining the canal. The contract for the section of the canal including the locks was awarded to Thomas Sheasby senior and the

176 *Farmers Bridge Locks.* locks were completed by November 1787. Until the building of the Tame Valley Canal in 1844 the locks formed the only link between the western and eastern sections of the Birmingham Canal Navigations and were very heavily used. In 1803 six men were employed to assist boats through the locks and in 1818 gas lighting was installed to allow night working. In March 1841, 4,877 boats passed through the top lock. There is an attractive toll house adjacent to the top lock. The towpath down the locks is now a busy pedestrian route. (HEW 1910)

WM 5. Gas Street Basin (SP 065864), a much visited canal basin, is the only surviving original basin of the Birmingham Canal and opened in 1772 when the basin was known as Brick Kiln Piece. The basin currently extends between Gas Street and Bridge Street but originally extended further to the east beyond Bridge Street to extensive wharves, but these have been filled in and built over. Evidence of the entrance to these wharves can be seen in the blocked bridges on the east side of the basin. On the west side of the basin is a range of contemporary brick buildings including the old toll office and the offices of the Worcester & Birmingham Canal Company. The basin is intersected by a

177 *Gas Street Basin, Birmingham.*

narrow strip of land, the Worcester Bar. The basin to the south of this land was that of the Worcester & Birmingham Canal, opened in 1795, and for 20 years the Birmingham Canal would not allow a physical connection between the two waterways. Consequently all goods passing between the two canals had to be unloaded, carried across the bar and re-loaded on the other side. In 1815 a lock was built through the bar, the chamber of which still exists although the gates have been removed. In recent years much of the land surrounding the basin has been redeveloped. There was another major basin to the north east, the site of which is now occupied by Baskerville House. (HEW 1528)

WM 6. Gravelly Hill Interchange (SP 095903). In August 1968 work started on the construction of what was to become, at that time, the largest motorway interchange in Britain. It connects the M6 Midland Links motorway to the A38(M) Aston Expressway leading into central Birmingham. There are also connections to the A38 Tyburn Road, the A5127 Gravelly Hill road and the A5127 Lichfield Road. For the M6 and A38(M) all

178 *Holliday Street Aqueduct, Worcester & Birmingham Canal.*

turning movements are provided with a separate path; that is all interactions between traffic streams are by diverging or merging movements only. An adjacent roundabout provides the other links. The interchange structures also cross a railway line and Salford Bridge canal junction. All the roads which form the interchange are elevated on concrete columns, with heights of up to 80ft. The scheme was designed by the Ministry of Transport Road Construction Unit at Leamington Spa and the contractors were A. Monk & Company of Warrington.

WM 7. Holliday Street Aqueduct (SP 064865), built by a railway company, has an interesting history and carries the Worcester & Birmingham

Canal over Holliday Street. In 1876 the Birmingham West Suburban Railway was opened as a long branch line from Lifford to Granville Street, just west of the canal. Five years later an extension of the railway to New Street station was constructed, requiring the construction of a railway tunnel and the aqueduct. The structure has a span of 42ft but is 156ft wide. The canal is carried on the western side of the aqueduct; the remaining section, approximately 100ft, was originally occupied by a road and a wharf. The aqueduct has 24 cast-iron columns cast by Handyside of Derby, the columns supporting transverse riveted wrought-iron I-section plate girders. From the base of the girders brick jack arches span between the girders and support the cast-iron bed plates of the canal. The east end of the aqueduct is on a slight curve, necessitating a complex arrangement of transverse beams at that end. The fascia of the aqueduct is nicely decorated with lozenge patterns with a band of similar decoration at the foot of the columns. (HEW 1651)

WM 8. Hollymoor Hospital Water Tower (SP003785) was built in 1905 to serve Hollymoor Hospital, then a part of Birmingham City Lunatic Asylum. It is a tall square tower in red brick with stone courses and a copper domed roof. The roof is topped with a lantern. The hospital was designed by William Martin & Martin and built by John Bowen & Sons. The hospital closed in 1994 and most of the buildings were demolished in 1996 to make way for a housing development. The tower is Listed Grade 2 and is currently in use for dental and medical facilities. The tower is not accessible to the public but may be viewed from the surrounding roads.

179   Hollymoor Hospital Water Tower.

WM 9. Kings Norton stop lock (SP 056795) is a rare example of a canal lock with guillotine gates. When a new canal was to make a junction with an existing canal it was normal for the older canal company to require a shallow lock to be built by the new canal company at or near to the junction. This lock, known as a stop lock, would normally have a very small difference in level arranged so that the new canal was at a higher level than the old. This ensured that water passed from the new canal to the old each time the lock was used. Such a lock is situated on the Stratford-upon-Avon Canal under Lifford Lane Bridge, about 200 yards east of its junction with the Worcester & Birmingham Canal. The lock is distinctive in having vertically rising guillotine gates at both ends. As the difference in level between the two canals was only a few inches there was no need for paddle gear, the gates being raised slightly to allow water to flow into and out of the lock. The wooden gates are held in cast-iron frames, sloped slightly towards the centre of the lock. The gates were raised and lowered by chain winches on the north side of the lock, their weight being counterbalanced by weights on the south side. The Engineer for this section

180   Kings Norton stop lock, Stratford-upon-Avon Canal.

of the Stratford Canal was Josiah Clowes. The water level in the two canals is now equal, consequently the lock is no longer in use, the gates being permanently raised. The lock can be accessed from Lifford Lane Bridge. (HEW 975)

WM 10. Lee Bridge and Winson Green Bridge (SP 047877 & SP 043878) These two adjacent large bridges on the Birmingham Canal are fine examples of bridge building in skew brickwork. They carry Dudley Road and Winson Green Road over a section of the canal built by Thomas Telford to cut off a long loop of the original line of the canal to the north. They both bear date stones of 1826 and have segmental brick arches springing from low brick walls. The square spans of both bridges are 53ft, the skew spans being 68ft and 73ft respectively. The deep arch rings have a sandstone keystone and the coursing of the skew arch brickwork is very fine. The corners of the arch are formed of sandstone blocks. The contractor for the work was Thomas Townshend and Telford's resident engineer was William Mackenzie. Thomas Eyres Lee was the solicitor to the Birmingham Canal Company at the time of the building of the bridge. (HEW 1704 & 1705)

181 *Winson Green Bridge, Birmingham Canal.*

WM 11. Sarehole Mill (SP 099818) is the last remaining of many mills in the valley of the River Cole in Birmingham. The preserved buildings date from about 1765 but there have been mills on this site since the 1500s. There are two wheels; the north wheel is a 12ft-diameter, five-foot-wide breast shot wheel with the water entering the wheel above the wheel centre. This wheel drove three pairs of millstones on the first floor of the mill. The south wheel similarly drove two pairs of millstones by way of the normal arrangement of gears, the wheel driving the pit wheel with a wallower gear and spur gear transferring the drive to the vertical shaft turning the millstones. This shaft also provided power for the sack hoist and the dressing machines used in the final preparation of the flour. Although it was used for most of its life for grinding grain, the mill was also used at various times for rolling

182 *Sarehole Mill, Birmingham.*

183 *Birchills Aqueduct.*

sheet metal, grinding bone for fertiliser and drawing wire. From 1756 to 1761 it was tenanted by Matthew Boulton, who at that time was involved with the family business, then situated in Snow Hill, Birmingham. He probably used the mill for rolling sheet metal until the business was transferred to the new Soho Manufactory in Birmingham, which became famous for the production of metal goods and later, after the establishment of the partnership with James Watt, the manufacture of steam engines. In 1851 the Sarehole Mill was extensively repaired and a steam engine installed. In 1919 the mill ceased working and in 1946 was bequeathed to Birmingham City Council; a restoration project was started in the 1960s. It was reopened in 1969 as a working museum, the north wheel still operational. The mill is open to the public from Easter to the end of October (except Mondays) and is free of charge.

BIRCHILLS

WM 12. Birchills Aqueduct (SK 009005) is a cast-iron and brick aqueduct which carries the line of the Wyrley & Essington Canal over the South Staffordshire Railway line from Walsall to Cannock. There is some evidence that the aqueduct may have been built off the original line of the canal, which was then diverted to pass over it. The aqueduct has a rectangular cast-iron trough supported by six cast-iron beams. The trough is in two spans of 14ft, each span being made up from three sections with bolted joints and there is a central pier in blue brickwork. The waterway is flanked on both sides by towpath areas supported on cast-iron plates which span between the edge of the trough and a single span cast-iron beam with a horizontal upper member and a curved lower member, crossing the railway in a single span of 31ft. The aqueduct bears an inscription on the outer edge of the beams recording that it was cast by Lloyds Foster & Co., engineers of nearby Wednesbury, and the date, 1856. The railway was authorised in 1854 and opened to traffic in 1858. The Engineer of the South Staffordshire Railway at that time was John Robinson McClean who was involved in schemes for railways, water supply, docks and drainage. He was President of the Institution of Civil Engineers in 1865. The aqueduct can be viewed from the bridge over the railway at Forest Lane, off the B4210 Bloxwich Road. (HEW 830)

BROWNHILLS

WM 13. Brownhills Aqueduct (SK 053065) is unusual in that it was built over an existing railway, although the railway and canal were opened only a year apart. The South Staffordshire Railway opened its line from Walsall to Wychnor junction on 9 April 1849. The following year the Wyrley & Essington Canal opened a new branch, the Anglesey Branch, from Ogley junction to Chasewater Reservoir. Where the canal crossed the railway a cast-iron aqueduct was erected that is almost identical to the later (1856) aqueduct at Birchills (see above), the waterway being carried in a two-span cast-iron trough with single-span cast-iron beams supporting the outer towpath areas. It is reasonable to assume that, as for Birchills Aqueduct, the ironwork was probably cast by Lloyd Foster & Co. although there is no corresponding inscription on this aqueduct. (HEW 283)

COVENTRY

WM 14. Alpha House (SP 352798) is the first multi-storey building in the world to be built by the 'jack block' system. It is a 17-storey residential tower block and contains 96 flats. There is a central core containing the lifts, stairs, refuse disposal chutes and other services. The principle of the jack block system is that the roof slab and the uppermost section of the core is cast at ground level. When the concrete has achieved sufficient strength, usually after about three days, the whole structure is jacked up by hydraulic jacks until it has reached one storey in height. The next floor is then added below and the process repeated, thus the building slowly rises from the ground. When the last (lowest) floor was being lifted into place the whole weight of the building, about 7,600 tons, had to be raised. While the lower floors are still being cast, it is then possible for the finishing trades to be at work on the completed upper floors. The building was completed in 1963. The system was developed by Felix Adler of Richard Costain (Construction) Ltd and the Coventry City Architect was Arthur Ling. (HEW 2652)

WM 15. Binley Road Bridge (SP 369786), a rather plain bridge, is a very early example of reinforced concrete bridge construction. Unfortunately later road widening has obscured the southern face of the bridge but the

184   *Brownhills Aqueduct.*

185   *Alpha House, Coventry.*

186   *Binley Road Bridge, Coventry.*

northern face is still visible. The bridge was built in 1911 and is a single reinforced concrete arch of 36ft span which carries the A428 road over the River Sowe. The arch is generally of segmental form, the thickness of the arch varying from 11 inches at the abutments to seven inches at the crown. The bridge was designed by L.G. Mouchel using the Hennebique system and the contractors were Messrs Lambrick & Co. of Burton upon Trent. The local newspaper records that the bridge was load-tested using four Daimler lorries loaded to 6¼ tons each and two steam rollers weighing a total of 27 tons. The vehicles were driven across the bridge in a group and the maximum deflection of the arch was recorded as only $\frac{1}{2}$ of an inch, well within the allowable limits. In 1965 the Binley Road was widened and a new bridge with horizontal concrete beams was built alongside the older bridge on the south side. At the same time the older bridge was given a two-inch-thick coating of sprayed cement on the underside and on some sections of the north face of the arch. (HEW 2152)

WM 16. Coat of Arms Bridge (SP 325767) is an elegant bridge and a local landmark. In 1842 and 1843 the London & Birmingham Railway obtained authorisation for a branch

line from Coventry to Milverton, near Warwick, later extended to Leamington Spa. Just south of Styvechale Common the line crossed a road called Cocks Lane. An ornate three-span masonry bridge was erected to carry the line over the road, built in rock-faced masonry with semi-elliptical brick arches. The centre span is 30ft and the two side spans 20ft. On the stone parapet wall on the bridge is a large coat of arms bearing the motto 'Vigilance'. This is the coat of arms of the Gregory family who owned the land through which the railway passed. It is presumed that the ornate style of the bridge was a form of compensation to Mr A.P. Gregory for the loss of his land. The bridge now gives its name to the road, Coat of Arms Bridge Road, which passes underneath it. The Engineer for the construction of the line was Robert Dockray, who had been one of Robert Stephenson's assistant engineers on the building of the London & Birmingham and was responsible for the planning and construction of several branch lines. (HEW 1030)

187 *Coat of Arms Bridge, Coventry.*

WM 17. Coventry Canal Basin (SP 333796). In 1769 the Coventry Canal opened to its terminal basin, which has a number of interesting features, just north of Coventry city centre. The basin has two arms providing 1,440ft of wharf space and on the south-east side is flanked by a range of two-storey warehouses 400ft long which were erected by about 1807. The warehouse buildings are in red brick with slate roofs and in some cases are canopied out over the waterway. Advantage was taken of the sloping site to position the loading bays in the warehouses a few feet lower than the waterway thus assisting the transfer of cargoes from canal to road. The canal company's offices were built at the basin in 1788 but were demolished in 1956. A small office and weighbridge is sited at the entrance to the basin. In the 1990s the basin was extensively restored and redeveloped. In particular a new range of buildings was erected on the north side of the basin which now houses shops and offices. A car park has been created on land to the north of the basin. (HEW 1527)

DUDLEY

WM 18. Dudley Canal Tunnel (SO 933893 to SO 946918) is a major canal tunnel with unusual links to underground limestone mines. In 1775 Lord Dudley and Ward built a short branch canal from the Birmingham Canal to his limestone quarries at Castle Hill, Dudley. The canal passed through a short tunnel into an open basin. In 1735 an Act was obtained authorising a tunnel under Dudley Hill to link the Birmingham Canal to the Dudley Canal south of the hill with Lord Dudley's tunnel forming the first section. Work on driving the tunnel and constructing the approach canal on the south side began in July 1785, the line of the tunnel being set out by John Snape and Abraham Lees under the supervision of the consulting engineer, Thomas Dadford senior. The tunnel contractor was John Pinkerton but the ground proved harder than expected and he was removed from the contract in September 1787. A shareholder, Isaac Pratt of Worcester, then spent 1½ years using direct labour but making no better progress until in June 1789 Josiah Clowes, an experienced and competent engineer, took over. The tunnel is 3,172 yards long and was the fifth longest canal tunnel in England when it was finally completed in June 1792. It is only wide enough for one boat and has been affected by mining subsidence which has reduced the maximum height of boats allowed to navigate the tunnel. The tunnel section varies along its length with some sections being brick-lined and others unlined. To partly overcome the subsidence problem the southernmost 209 yards were rebuilt to larger dimensions in 1884. At its northern end the open Castle Mill basin is the focal point for a series of underground canals penetrating into the limestone mines, the most important of which was the 1,185-yard tunnel driven south-west to Wrens Nest mine. The tunnel was closed to traffic in 1962 but the formation of the Dudley Canal Trust led to the restoration of the tunnel and it reopened in 1973. Boats were propelled through the tunnel by 'legging' or 'shafting' but later a tug was provided. Modern trips into the tunnel use electrically powered narrow boats. (HEW 670)

WM 19. Netherton Tunnel (SO 954883 to SO 967909) was the last major canal tunnel of the Canal Age and is still one of the largest built in Britain. It passes under the limestone ridge at Dudley and was built to provide an alternative route to the Dudley Tunnel (see above) between the Dudley Canal to the south and the Birmingham canal system to the north. The tunnel is 3,207 yards long and construction started at the end of 1855 using 17 working shafts, of which seven were retained for ventilation. The tunnel was opened on 20 August 1858 after a remarkably short construction period of only 31 months. The tunnel has large dimensions, the waterway being 17ft wide, allowing two narrowboats travelling in opposite directions to pass, and two towpaths giving

an overall width of 27ft. The tunnel is brick-lined throughout, the lining varying in thickness from 22 to 27in. The Engineer was James Walker, the second President of the Institution of Civil Engineers, who had a distinguished career as a civil engineer including acting as consulting engineer to Trinity House from 1825 to 1862. The contractor was George Meakin. The tunnel required extensive repairs in the 1980s due to the

188 *Tipton Lift Bridge, Black Country Museum.*

upward movement of the brick-lined base. In 2008 celebrations were held at the tunnel to mark the 150th anniversary of its opening. Just beyond the south portal of the tunnel is an interesting set of four cast-iron arch bridges carrying the towpaths of the canals at the junction. (HEW 669)

WM 20. Tipton Lift Bridge (SO 948917), a fine example of a vertical lift bridge and now located at the Black Country Museum, was originally built by the Great Western Railway to cross an arm of the canal basin adjacent to the Chain Proof House near Bloomfield canal junction in Tipton. The bridge deck, 27ft 6in long and 12ft, wide is

raised vertically by chains which pass over pulleys mounted at the top of four steel columns. There are two counter weights of six tons each hung from the other ends of the lifting chains. The bridge is raised by a winch, coupled by a complex system of drive shafts, gears and a short chain drive to the two shafts upon which are mounted the chain pulleys. The bridge was designed in the office of the Chief Engineer of the GWR, the steelwork was fabricated at Armstrong's works in Glasgow and the machinery at their works in Newcastle upon Tyne. The bridge was probably in use by 1922. In 1954 the basin closed, the bridge at that time being in a poor condition with sideways buckling of all four vertical columns. It was removed from the site to Shugborough, whence it was transferred to the Black Country Museum, repaired and re-erected across an arm of the museum's canal system. (HEW 1225)

HAMPTON IN ARDEN
WM 21. Hampton in Arden Pack Horse Bridge (SP 215801) is a good example of a bridge designed for the use of pack horses, an important mode of long-distance freight transport in medieval times. The bridge is only six feet wide and carries a trackway from Bradnocks Marsh to

189 Hampton in Arden Pack Horse Bridge.

Hampton in Arden over the River Blythe. There is a total of five masonry arches, three being pointed arches and two, presumably later, segmental arches. The spans of the arches vary from 9ft 9in to 10ft 2in. The bridge probably dates from the 15th century and has been extensively repaired over the intervening years. (HEW 1529)

SMETHWICK
WM 22. Engine Arm Aqueduct (SP 024888) is a fine example of a design by Thomas Telford for an iron aqueduct carrying one canal over another. It was designed in the late 1820s when Telford was carrying out extensive improvements to the main line of the Birmingham Canal. As part of these improvements a new low-level canal was driven in a deep cutting through the high ground at Smethwick. Where this new canal cut across the line of a short branch canal from the old main line to a pumping station, a cast-iron aqueduct was constructed with a single arch spanning 52ft. The waterway is carried in a cast-iron trough with paved towpaths on both sides. There are five

190 Engine Arm Aqueduct, Birmingham Canal.

191 *Galton Bridge, Birmingham Canal.*

192 *Rabone Lane Towpath Bridges, Birmingham Canal.*

arch ribs, each cast in four sections with bolted joints. The arch ribs have radial struts between the arch and the trough. Above the arch ribs on the external faces of the aqueduct there is a series of vertical columns with pointed arches which support the towpath areas. It was completed in 1829, the ironwork being cast by the local Horseley Company. The whole structure is nicely detailed and the arch bears a resemblance to the arch of Cantlop Bridge in Shropshire (see above). It can be viewed from the towpaths of the two canals. (HEW 492)

WM 23. Galton Bridge (SP 015893). In order to carry Roebuck Lane over the deep cutting of his new low-level canal (see below), Thomas Telford designed one of his most famous bridges, Galton Bridge. The bridge crosses the cutting at its deepest part and the roadway is about 65ft above the waterway. The single cast-iron segmental arch spans 150ft and has six arch ribs, each made up from seven segments with bolted joints. The rib segments are cast with an X-lattice and the spandrel space between the arch and roadway is filled with struts arranged in an intersecting pattern. A notable feature of the bridge is in the positioning of the masonry abutments, about halfway down the cutting sides: a bold decision that was a compromise between a very long span with the abutments sited at the top of the embankment and a smaller span but with very tall abutments founded at the bottom of the cutting. Even so, the span was one of the largest in the world when the bridge was completed in 1829. The design of the bridge is identical to that for other Telford bridges in Scotland and England, at least ten being recorded. The iron work for Galton Bridge was cast at Horseley Ironworks nearby, although the castings for all the other similar bridges were cast by William Hazledine at Shrewsbury. In 1975 a new road was built parallel to the bridge to the east and Galton Bridge is now restricted to pedestrian traffic. It is named after Samuel

Tertius Galton, a member of the Committee of the Birmingham Canal Navigation Company. (HEW 421)

WM 24. Rabone Lane Canal Junction Bridges (SP 029890) are representative examples of many similar bridges to be found all over the Birmingham canal network. Between Rabone Lane and Bridge Street is the junction between the original main line of the Birmingham Canal and Thomas Telford's new low-level canal through Smethwick Cutting (see below). In order to carry the towpaths of the two canals over the junction two identical cast-iron footbridges were built in 1828. They have semi-elliptical arches with a span of 52ft 6in and two external arch ribs which also form the bridge parapets, each rib cast in two sections with a joint at the crown of the arch. The ribs have an X-lattice separating the flanges with a decorative quatrefoil pattern above the lattice. The deck is formed of cast-iron plates with ribs cast on the upper surface to retain the gravel filling of the footway. They were cast by Horseley Ironworks. The bridge parapets are heavily scored by tow ropes. (HEW 1197)

WM 25. Smethwick Cutting (SO 996899 to SP 029890) is an impressive canal cutting 3,982 yards long and up to 66ft deep. It was excavated to carry Thomas Telford's new canal through the hill at Smethwick. The original and very short summit level of the Birmingham Canal at Smethwick when opened in 1772 was at 491ft above sea level but this was lowered 18ft by John Smeaton in 1789 to 473ft. In his review of the state of the canal in the 1820s Thomas Telford recommended the cutting of a new low-level canal a further 20ft lower at 453ft to eliminate the existing summit locks. The new canal is 40ft wide and has towpaths on both sides to allow horse-drawn boats travelling in opposite directions to pass without unhitching one of the tow ropes. The cutting was dug by hand and a fascinating document in the Mackenzie archive at the Institution of Civil Engineers records on a longitudinal section of the cutting the sequence of the

193 Smethwick Cutting, Birmingham Canal.

excavation with the date when each block of excavation was completed. The earliest date shown is April 1827 and the latest date is August 1829. A hand-written note on the drawing indicates that the water was first let into the canal on Sunday evening, 8 February 1829. William Mackenzie was Telford's resident engineer for the Birmingham Canal improvements. Both the 473ft and 453ft levels are still in use. (HEW 1875)

WM 26. Spon Lane Lock Flight (SO 999899). This flight of three locks is the oldest existing set of locks on the old main line of the Birmingham Canal. It is situated to the west of Spon Lane and is today located partly underneath the M5 viaduct. The locks extend over a distance of about 650 yards and carry the canal down from the Smethwick summit to join the low-level canal at Bromford junction. The total fall is 20ft. They are conventional narrow locks with single-leaf top gates and double-mitred bottom gates. There are both gate and ground paddles. Below the tail of the bottom lock there is one of the familiar cast-iron towpath bridges marked 'Horseley Ironworks 1829'. These locks were originally on the Birmingham Canal's branch to Wednesbury, which was the first section of the canal to open on 6 November 1769. The locks can be seen by following the towpath of the canal from the bridge on Spon Lane. (HEW 1964)

194 Bottom lock of Spon Lane Locks, Birmingham Canal.

WM 27. Steward Aqueduct (SP 002898). Aqueducts carrying one canal over another are rare but there are two within a short distance of one another in Smethwick. To the west of Spon Lane Bridge the old line of the Birmingham Canal crosses the Telford line 20ft below by way of a two-span brick structure built in about 1829. The skew spans have semi-elliptical arches in engineering bricks with stone voussoirs on the outside edges of the arches. The somewhat massive arches are required to carry the full weight of the canal and its puddled clay bed and it is interesting to compare this aqueduct with Engine Arm Aqueduct (see above), a much lighter structure in iron situated on the same canal about 1½ miles to the east. The contractor was Thomas Townshend, who was responsible for much of the improvement work on the canal in the 1820s. (HEW 1904)

195 Water Orton Bridge.

WATER ORTON

WM 28 Water Orton Bridge (SP 174914) is unusual in that, unlike most medieval bridges, it has not been widened for modern traffic. It is located on the road from Water Orton to Minworth, where it crosses the River Tame. The bridge dates from the 16th century and is said to have been built with stone from the destroyed house of Bishop Vesey at Sutton Coldfield. It has six arches, all segmental, in red sandstone, the two outermost arches being dry in times of normal river flow. The spans of the arches vary from 13ft 6in to 14ft 2in and there are substantial cut waters on both faces of

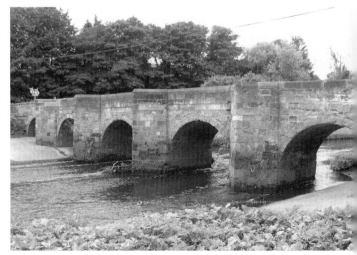

the bridge which are extended upwards to form pedestrian refuges. These are necessary as the roadway is only 8ft 8in wide and is suitable for one-way traffic only. The parapet wall, about two feet high, is of a paler stone than the rest of the bridge which may indicate rebuilding at some time.

WEST BROMWICH

WM 29. Taylor's or Grand Junction Aqueduct (SP 018949) is a rare example of a large canal aqueduct which was built over an already existing railway. The Tame Valley Canal was built to bypass the congested locks at Farmers Bridge (see above) and just south of Tame Bridge Parkway station it crosses the line of the Grand Junction Railway. The aqueduct is an impressive structure, with three spans mainly in brick. The segmental

196 *Taylor's Aqueduct.*

arches are on a skew angle with a square span of 32ft. The outer voussoirs of the arches, the parapet coping and string course are in sandstone. Towpaths are provided on both sides of this canal which was built to standards more applicable to railway building, with high embankments and deep cuttings. The aqueduct dates from February 1844, 17 years after the opening of the railway. It can be viewed from the end of the platform at Tame Bridge Parkway station or from Bustlehome Lane bridge to the south-east. The towpath can be accessed from Beacon View Road. (HEW 1909)

WOLVERHAMPTON

WM 30. Chillington Wharf (SO 926981) canal basin is, as far as can be ascertained, the only surviving example in its original form of one of the canal-railway interchange basins once numerous on the Birmingham canal network. It began its life as a single basin built in 1829 to serve a nearby ironworks, linked to the basin by a narrow-gauge tramway. It was extended into a long and a short basin about 1848, then in about 1886 the basin was purchased by the London & North Western Railway and converted for use as an interchange basin by constructing a branch line from the nearby Stour Valley line. The basin was rebuilt in about 1902. One of the two arms of the basin was removed in

197 *Chillington Wharf, Wolverhampton.*

the 1930s when the present overhead crane was installed. The basin is about 200ft long and about 30ft wide at its western end, reducing to about 23ft wide at the end furthest from the canal. Railway lines are laid along both sides of the basin, the rail tracks set

a few feet below the level of the canal enabling goods to be transhipped on the level between the railway wagons and the canal boats. The narrower section of the basin and the adjacent railway tracks on the south side are covered by a two-span gable-ended overall roof with open sides supported on steel stanchions. At the west end the basin is joined to the main line of the canal by a short link under a bridge carrying the towpath of the main canal. The basin is on private land but can be viewed from the towpath bridge which is accessed from the nearby A41 Bilston Road. (HEW 2379)

WM 31. Tunstall (Dunstall) Water Bridge (SJ 898006) is a very unusual bridge over the Staffordshire & Worcestershire Canal, carrying both a footway and the Smestow Brook over the canal. It was a particularly tricky problem of setting out as the brook drove an undershot wheel at Tunstall Mill just upstream and was required to pass over the canal to power watermills downstream. Effectively, it determined the level of the summit pound of the canal. It was built from March 1769 by James Brindley with John Fennyhouse Green as his assistant after the original bridge built in 1766 had collapsed. The drawings of both old and new bridges still exist and show how design had progressed during construction of this, one of the first main-line canals. The original had no towpath through it, like the earliest canal bridges at Wightwick, Compton and Bumblehole, but its replacement was more generous, akin to those from Prestwood to the south, Coven to the north and also on other Brindley canals such as the Droitwich. The bridge is built in brick and the segmental arch has a span of about 25ft. The bridge originally carried the brook in a brick channel on the north side of the bridge. The channel was about seven feet wide and the central portion of the brick arch under the water channel was at some time formed of a cast-iron arch segment. On the south side of the bridge was a footway about 11ft wide with a connection to the towpath on the west side of the bridge. In 1995-6 the bridge was extensively altered. A second water channel was created by constructing a new brick wall about seven feet to the south of the original south channel wall. The wall between the two water channels was lowered to the east and west of the bridge to form overflow weirs allowing surplus water from the Smestow Brook to enter the new channel, from where it flows by a stepped cascade on the west side of the bridge to a new concrete pipe culvert. The footway was correspondingly reduced in width to 3ft 6in. The area today is known as Dunstall but the plaque on the bridge refers to it as Tunstall Water Bridge No. 63. (HEW 23)

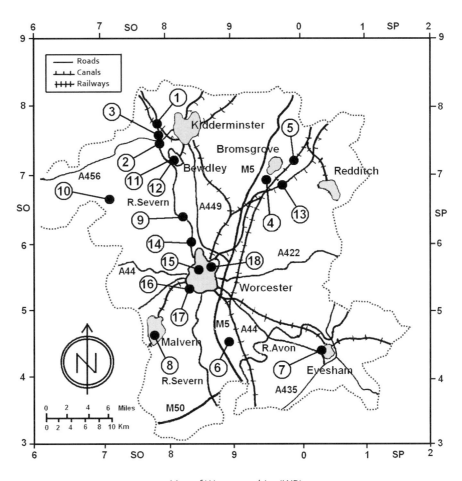

Map of Worcestershire (WR)

WR1. Victoria Railway Bridge, Arley
WR2. Bewdley Bridge
WR3. Elan Valley Pipeline Bridge, Bewdley
WR4. Danzey Green Windmill
WR5. Lickey Incline, Bromsgrove
WR6. Croome Court Bridges
WR7. Evesham New Bridge
WR8. Great Malvern Station
WR9. Holt Fleet Bridge, Ombersley
WR10. Stanford Bridge
WR11. Stourport Canal Basins
WR12. Severn Bridge, Stourport
WR13. Tardebigge Lock Flight
WR14. Bevere Bridge, Worcester
WR15. Foregate Street Railway Bridge, Worcester
WR16. Powick New Bridge
WR17. Powick Old Bridge
WR18. Rainbow Hill Bridge, Worcester

ARLEY
WR1. Victoria Railway Bridge (SO 767792), situated on the preserved Severn Valley railway over the River Severn just south of Upper Arley, was the longest cast-iron arch railway bridge in Britain when it was completed. The bridge has a single cast-iron arch of 200ft, completed in 1861. The arch has four I-section ribs, each of nine bolted segments, four feet deep. The deck is supported from the arch by vertical struts. The abutments are massive stone blocks which are each pierced by a single brick arch to allow access along the river bank. However, the towpath, which is on the west bank, is carried round the abutment by a walkway built out into the river. The bridge was built by the Severn Valley Railway Company, later part of the Great Western Railway. The bridge bears an inscription at the centre of the arch recording that it was erected in 1861 to a design by John (later Sir John) Fowler and was cast and erected by the Coalbrookdale Company. The contractor for the building of the railway was Thomas Brassey. There is a near-twin bridge, Albert Edward Bridge, located at Telford in Shropshire and built three years later (see above). (HEW 464)

BEWDLEY
WR 2. Bewdley Bridge (SO 788755). There has been a bridge over the River Severn at Bewdley since 1447 but this bridge was destroyed in 1459 and replaced by a timber bridge in 1460, rebuilt in 1483 and repaired in 1644 after damage during the Civil War. In 1795 the bridge was partly destroyed by a severe flood on the river and Thomas Telford designed the present bridge to replace it. The bridge has three main spans in sandstone, the central segmental arch having a span of 59ft 9in (Telford's drawing states the span to be 60ft) and the two side spans 50ft 7in. On either side of the main bridge there are two small arches which carry the approach road of the bridge over the towpaths. The eastern approach to the bridge runs parallel to the river on an approach viaduct of 12 semi-circular arches of seven-foot span before turning to cross the river. The bridge is an elegant, well-proportioned bridge with a balustraded stone parapet.

199 *Victoria Bridge, Severn Valley Railway.*

200 *River Severn, Bewdley Bridge.*

201 *Elan Valley Pipeline Bridge, Bewdley.*

It was built, allegedly in one season, by John Simpson, a stonemason of Midlothian who came to Shrewsbury in 1790. He began working for Thomas Telford in 1793 and continued an association with him for the rest of his working life. (HEW 461)

WR 3. Elan Valley Pipeline Bridge (SO 775782). Just to the north of Bewdley the River Severn is crossed by a large steel arch bridge. The bridge is unusual in that it supports the pipeline carrying water 73½ miles to Birmingham from the Elan Valley reservoirs in Wales. It has a single segmental steel arch of 150ft span, the four riveted arch ribs having a lattice structure between the bottom and top flanges. The arch rib is large, measuring 4ft 9in in depth. The bridge dates from 1904 and was designed by James Mansergh, the Engineer for the water supply scheme. It was designed to carry six 42in-diameter pipelines but initially only two were installed. Later a 60in-diameter pipe was completed in 1939 and a further 60in-diameter pipe in 1991. The pipeline bridge is at the lowest point on the aqueduct, which flows by gravity from Wales to Birmingham, and the pressure in the steel pipes at the river crossing is 250lb per square inch. The bridge can be seen from the end of the narrow lane running north from Bewdley along the east bank of the river and parallel to the line of the Severn Valley Railway. (HEW 1195)

BROMSGROVE

WR 4. Danzey Green Windmill (SO 952683), a post mill, is one of the few working windmills in the region and originally stood in a derelict state at Tanworth in Arden, Warwickshire, disused since the 1870s. It was dismantled and removed to the Avoncroft Museum of Buildings at Bromsgrove in 1969 where it was restored to full working order. It was probably built in the early part of the 19th century and has a red brick circular base with timber upper works. The upper part of the mill is supported on a massive post, in turn supported by four cross-timbers resting on plinths built out from the brick wall. The whole of the top section of the mill is rotated by a hand-operated winch to bring the sails into the wind, a long diagonal beam extending from the rear of the mill and terminating in a wheel running on a timber track. There are four sails spanning 60ft which were originally common sails with canvas curtains, but it was rebuilt with two common and two spring sails. The external finish to the side walls is weatherboarding.

The mechanism is the standard type for a post mill: a main timber shaft with a brake wheel which drives a vertical shaft via a wallower gear. The vertical shaft drives the mill stones. The mill can be seen when the museum is open to visitors. There is an admission charge. (HEW 864)

WR 5. Lickey Incline (SO 969693 to SO 992720) is the longest adhesion-worked railway incline in Britain and also one of the steepest. A major difficulty facing the planners of the Birmingham & Gloucester Railway was the descent from the high ground of the Birmingham plateau to the valley of the River Severn at Bromsgrove. The decision was made to carry the line down a steep incline two miles long falling at a gradient of 1 in 37.7 (2.65 per cent) from Blackwell to Bromsgrove station through a vertical height of about 300ft. The alignment of the incline is straight, mostly on embankment, with shallow cuttings at the top and bottom. The Engineer of the line was Capt. William S. Moorsom, who was involved in a number of other railway schemes in Britain and Ireland. The section of the line including the Lickey Incline was opened on 17 September 1840. To work the trains up and down the incline special locomotives were imported from America, of 4-2-0 wheel arrangement, which could haul 33-ton loads at 12 to 15 m.p.h. They were replaced in 1845 by *Great Britain* with an 0-6-0 wheel arrangement capable of hauling 135 tons at 8 to 10 m.p.h. Further 0-6-0 banking engines were introduced in 1878 but increasing train weights required more powerful motive power. In 1891 Sir Henry Fowler designed a special 0-10-0 banking engine which, together with smaller engines, provided banking assistance up the incline until the end of steam-working in the 1960s. Most trains now climb the bank without assistance. (HEW 865)

202 Avoncroft Museum of Buildings, Danzey Green Windmill.

CROOME D'ABITOT

WR 6. Croome Court Bridges (SO 879447). In the grounds of Croome Court, now owned by the National Trust, there are two important wrought-iron bridges carrying footpaths over an ornamental lake. They date from 1795 and are, with Syon Park bridge mentioned below, the oldest wrought iron bridges known to remain in Britain. They show how the understanding of bridge design in a new material was developing. The larger of the two bridges has a span of 52ft 6in and is a very slender structure. The deck ribs are of flat plate 5in deep with stiffening pieces running along one side only. At each end of the rib a short segment with a circle in the spandrel connects the arch rib to the base of the

203 Croome Court Bridge.

204 *Evesham New Bridge.*

abutment. The timber deck is supported on cross-beams with diagonal stiffening. The smaller bridge is similar but of 25ft span. The ironwork was supplied and erected by John Mackell, a smith of Park Lane, London. There is no firm evidence of the designer but James Wyatt was the architect principally involved at Croome Court at the time and the bridges are similar to Wyatt's bridge of 1790 at Syon Court, Isleworth so it seems reasonable to assume he was the designer. Croome Park is open to the public at weekends and some weekdays at certain times of the year. There is an admission charge for non-members of the National Trust. (HEW 580)

EVESHAM

WR 7. Evesham New Bridge (SP 034431) is a fairly early large reinforced concrete bowstring girder bridge dating from 1928. It carries the A435 road over the River Avon to the south of the town. The main arch spans 110ft and is segmental in form with two arch ribs 2ft 6in wide and 4ft 6in deep at the arch ends. The bridge deck is suspended from the arch by reinforced concrete hangers 12in square, the deck rising in a slight curve to the centre of the bridge. The ends of the arch have decorative corner posts with concrete pillars that originally carried street lamps, now removed. On the north side of the bridge is an approach viaduct with 28 horizontal spans of 16ft with reinforced concrete beams. The bridge was built by Thomas Vale & Son Ltd and the Indented Bar & Concrete Engineering Company Ltd to a design by B.C. Hammond, the County Surveyor. (HEW 1700)

GREAT MALVERN

205 *Detail of column head at Great Malvern Station.*

WR 8. Great Malvern Station (SO 784457) is a delightful station on the line from Worcester to Hereford, a notable feature being the ornate decoration of its platform canopy. The main station buildings are situated on the north side of the line and are in masonry with a slate roof surmounted by a decorative ridge feature. The platform canopy has vertical cast-iron columns with decorative cast-iron beams and cantilevers supporting the timber roof. Nearly all the columns are decorated at the top by ornate tree leaf and flower patterns cast in high relief. Most of the patterns are different and are brightly painted. The station was opened in 1863 and the architect was E.W. Elmslie. The contractors were Brassey and Ballard. (HEW 1113)

OMBERSLEY

WR 9. Holt Fleet Bridge (SO 824634), one of Thomas Telford's standard bridge designs with an interesting history of strengthening, carries the A4133 road over the River Severn west of the village of Ombersley and was erected in 1828. It has a single cast-iron arch spanning 150ft, almost identical to Galton Bridge in Smethwick (see above). The arch has five ribs each consisting of seven segments with bolted joints. The roadway is supported by diagonal intersecting struts forming an X-lattice. The sandstone abutments are pierced with flood arches which also allow the river towpath to pass the bridge, the abutment wall on the east bank showing deep cuts in the stonework caused by tow ropes. In the 1920s the lateral stiffness of the bridge was giving cause

for concern and the then County Surveyor of Worcestershire, Mr B.C. Hammond, devised a scheme for strengthening the bridge in conjunction with two French engineers, M. de Boulogne and M. Gueritte. The upper and lower faces of the arch were encased in a reinforced concrete slab extending over the full width of the bridge, the reinforcing steel bars being welded to the cast iron. Each of the more vertical of the spandrel struts was encased in concrete and a new reinforced concrete deck slab was cast on new cross-beams. The deck was widened by being cantilevered out to give a carriageway 18ft wide with two three-foot wide footways. This was the first time that this technique had been used in Britain and the work was carried out over 18 months by the Yorkshire Hennebique Company of Leeds. The bridge, despite these substantial alterations, still retains its characteristic Telford form. (HEW 135)

206 *Holt Fleet Bridge, River Severn.*

STANFORD

WR 10. Stanford Bridge (SO 714658) is the oldest reinforced concrete bridge in the region, built in 1905. It originally carried the B4203 road over the River Teme at Stanford. The span of the segmental arch is 96ft and the bridge is designed much in the style of an iron arch with three arch ribs 2ft 7in deep. The deck is supported from the arch by three vertical struts on both sides. It was built by the Hennebique Company, pioneers in the construction of reinforced concrete bridges in Britain. The bridge has been bypassed by a new concrete bridge a short distance to the east and is now used only by pedestrians. It is recorded that a brick and stone bridge with three arches replaced a wooden bridge built in 1548. The stone bridge was replaced in 1797 by a single 96ft-8in-span iron bridge built by the architect John Nash, an earlier replacement in 1795 having collapsed during construction. This bridge lasted until 1905 when the present bridge was completed. (HEW 1619)

STOURPORT

WR 11. Stourport Canal Basins (SO 811711). The town of Stourport was created at the location where the Staffordshire & Worcestershire Canal enters the River Severn and has an important place in canal history. The canal entered several large basins from the north, the basins also accessible by barge locks from the River Severn. Here goods could be transhipped between the narrow canal boats and the wide-beamed Severn barges for onward transhipment. The canal Engineer was James Brindley, with Thomas Dadford senior as the main contractor. The basins were developed over a number of years, the earliest (the Upper basin) being constructed contemporary with the canal in the period 1768-71. The barge locks were

207 *Narrow locks to River Severn in the Stourport Canal Basins.*

also built at this time. Later, further basins were added, the Clock basin and the narrow locks into the river being opened in 1781 and the last basin development, Mart Lane basin to the east, carried out prior to 1835. As originally built, the basins were surrounded by warehouses, toll offices and other buildings. Many of these have now been demolished but, of those that remain, two are worthy of particular note. The Clock warehouse is an elegant brick building surmounted by a timber clock tower (1812) and was originally used as a grain and general goods store. It is now the headquarters of a yacht club. The second building of note is the *Tontine Hotel*, a three-storey brick building standing on high ground overlooking the river. It was built at the time of the original basin (1771) as a commercial hotel. The original town of Stourport-on-Severn was largely a creation of the canal and contains many fine examples of the architecture and engineering of the late 18th century. Although the commercial traffic of the canal and river is now virtually extinct, the canal and basins are still much used for recreational use. Mart Lane basin, which was filled in in 1949 has now been excavated and restored to use together with new residential development. (HEW 1460)

208 *Stourport Bridge, River Severn.*

WR 12. River Severn Bridge (SO 808711) is an impressive cast-iron arch bridge carrying the A451 road over the River Severn in Stourport. The main river span is

a single segmental cast-iron arch of 160ft span. It has five ribs, each formed from five segments. The spandrel space between the arch and the roadway is elegantly designed with circles that increase in size towards the abutments and contain patterns of increasing complexity. The circle nearest the abutment contains a shield with the legend 'S B T 1870'. The arch is supported by massive sandstone abutments.

The approaches to the bridge are complex. On both sides of the bridge the roadway is carried on a low viaduct with segmental brick arches. On the north bank the viaduct has 28 arches and on the south side 10 arches. In addition on the south bank there is a smaller arch through the abutment immediately adjacent to the main bridge for the river towpath. There is a fine cast-iron circular staircase leading onto the bridge from the river bank at the north-west corner of the main bridge. The bridge was extensively refurbished during 2006-7. (HEW 1051)

TARDEBIGGE

WR 13. Tardebigge Lock Flight (SO 963680 to SO 995693). Extending over a distance of about 2¼ miles with a total fall of 217ft, this flight of 30 locks is the greatest narrow lock flight in Britain. The locks carry the Worcester & Birmingham Canal down from the high ground around Birmingham into the valley of the River Severn. They are the canal equivalent of the Lickey Incline on the nearby Birmingham & Gloucester Railway (see above). The locks are fairly evenly spaced, about 100 yards apart, and with the exception of the top lock are conventional narrow locks with a fall of about seven feet. The locks have single-leaf top gates and double-mitred bottom gates with two ground paddles at

the top gate and two gate paddles at the bottom gates. The top lock has a much greater fall, about 12ft, which makes it one of the deepest narrow locks on the canal system. The reason for the large fall at this lock is that it was the site of an experimental vertical lift which the Worcester & Birmingham Company were considering for use as an alternative to conventional locks. The lift, designed by John Woodhouse, consisted of a tank suspended by eight chains which passed over large wheels at the side of the lock chamber with counterbalance weights. The tank weighed 64 tons and was raised and lowered by a hand winch. Trials of the lift were held between 1808 and 1813 but the lift mechanism proved, in the words of John Rennie who reported on the lift, 'too delicate in its parts', and the decision was

209   Entering the top lock at Tarde-bigge Locks.

made in 1811 to build conventional locks. The lift was eventually removed in 1815. The canal had reached Tardebigge wharf, at the top of the locks, from Birmingham by March 1807 but was not completed to Worcester until December 1815. (HEW 768)

WORCESTER

WR 14. Bevere Bridge (SO 837594) is a cast-iron arch bridge carrying a farm track from the east bank of the River Severn to Bevere Island. The bridge was built about 1844 during improvements to the river navigation under an Act passed in 1842, when locks and weirs were built under the supervision of William Cubitt and Edward Leader Williams senior, including Bevere Lock. The bridge has a relatively large single span of 88ft 6in and the segmental arch has three ribs each made up from three segments. The bridge deck is supported by radial struts from the arch. The deck appears to be brick paving over timber but the deck is in poor condition with several holes. The brick-paved approach ramps to the bridge are similarly in poor condition. There is a neat decorative moulding at the foot of the cast-iron parapet rail. The bridge can be viewed by following the footpath from Bevere village down to the river bank then following the river bank footpath downstream to the bridge. The lock weir is immediately downstream of the bridge. (HEW 2683)

210   *Bevere Bridge, River Severn.*

211   *Foregate Street Bridge, Worcester.*

212   *Powick New Bridge, Worcester.*

WR 15. Foregate Street Railway Bridge (SO 849552), built in 1909, carries the railway from Foregate Street station to Malvern across Foregate Street in central Worcester. The span is 50ft 6in and at first glance the bridge appears to be a cast-iron arch. However, the main structure of the bridge is of steel with three riveted steel plate girders, the deck supported on corrugated steel trough units which span transversely between the main girders. The attractive cast-iron fascia of the bridge is supported by brackets from the outer edges of the girders and is in the form of an arch. The fascia is decorated with the arms of the Great Western Railway and the City of Worcester. The railway was opened in July 1859 by the Worcester & Hereford Railway which became a part of the West Midlands Railway in 1860 before being absorbed by the Great Western Railway in August 1863. The present bridge replaced an earlier structure. (HEW 1912)

WR 16. Powick New Bridge (SO 836524) was built to bypass the narrow medieval bridge over the River Teme at Powick, south of Worcester (see below) as a single-span cast-iron arch bridge with two adjacent flood arches in 1837. The main arch spans 68ft 8in and is segmental in form, with seven ribs each made up from three segments bolted together. The bridge deck is supported from the arch by an X-lattice. The cast-iron handrail has a decorative pillar at mid-span, below which is a coat of arms. The flood arches have nicely proportioned pointed arches of 15ft span with seven ribs, each cast in one piece with a single X-lattice in the spandrel and a horizontal top chord. The designer of the bridge was C.H. Capper of Birmingham and the contractors were Charles Faviell for the masonry and William Yates of Rotherham for the ironwork. (HEW 1620)

WR 17. Powick Old Bridge (SP 835524) is an ancient bridge with a significant history that once carried the main road south from Worcester towards Great Malvern over the River Teme, near to its confluence with the River Severn to the east. The bridge has two sections. The older section, over the river itself, has three skew spans of stone segmental arches with a brick parapet wall. The arches span 20ft between massive masonry piers with cutwaters on both sides of the bridge. The actual building date of this section is uncertain but there is a reference to the bridge at Powick as early as 1447. Immediately to the north of the older bridge, separated from it by a large block of masonry, is a two-span brick and stone bridge which originally spanned the outflow from a water mill sited just to the west of the bridge. The two segmental arches have a larger span of 25ft and are separated by a pier 18ft wide. The mill was replaced in 1894 by a water-turbine-powered electricity generating station, the largest hydro-electric power station in Britain when it opened and the first to serve the city of Worcester. The power station was also equipped with three steam

213 *Powick Old Bridge, Worcester.*

engines which could be used to generate electricity if the water flow in the river was too low or too high. The buildings remain, although no longer used for this purpose, and were converted into apartments in 2000. The old bridge was bypassed in 1837 by the iron bridge just downstream (see above). Powick Bridge was the site of the first major engagement of the Civil War in 1642. (HEW 2162)

WR 18. Rainbow Hill Bridge (SO 854555) is a bridge of unusual design which carries the railway line from Shrub Hill station to Foregate Street station in Worcester over the Worcester & Birmingham Canal and a road. The canal bridge is a brick segmental arch of 49ft 9in span over the canal and its towpath. To the west is a small semi-circular arch of 12ft span over the roadway, above which is a circular hole 12ft in diameter. The purpose of the hole is to reduce the weight of the bridge above the smaller arch. The whole bridge presents a pleasing appearance. The Engineers for the Worcester & Hereford Railway were Charles Liddell and Lewis Gordon and the contractors were Thomas Brassey and Stephen Ballard, who in partnership built other railways in the area. (HEW 1911)

214 *Rainbow Hill Bridge, Worcester.*

abutment – the masonry at each end of the arch which provides the resistance to the thrust of the arch.

accumulator, hydraulic – a large vertical cylinder/piston to pressurise a water power system; a heavy weight is raised to the top of the piston and the system is pressurised by the weight operating under gravity.

agger – a raised causeway upon which a Roman road was constructed.

aqueduct – a bridge carrying a watercourse over another watercourse, road, railway or valley.

arch dam – of masonry or concrete, used where the rock formations at the sides of the valley are able to support the thrust from the arch form, providing a more economical material and capable of being built to greater heights. Sound rock is also needed for the foundations.

arch types:

    elliptical – similar to segmental but with the centre portion flattened;

    pointed – two half-segments with radii displaced to opposite sides of arch, meeting at the centre at a sharp point, can be sharp or flat;

    relieving – an arch built into a structure to reduce the load on a wall below;

    semi-circular – formed of one half of a circle, rise equal to half the span;

    segmental – formed of less than half a circle, rise less than half the span;

    Tudor – each side formed of a short vertical length leading to a sharp curved corner and an upward-angled straight length to the centre.

asphalt – a high-strength road material of stone and binder of bitumen or natural asphalt.

balanced cantilever construction – the bridge is built in increments each side of a support pier. Construction can be either by casting the increments *in situ* using specially designed shuttering to form the hollow concrete sections or by casting the sections off-site and transporting and lifting into place. The method is particularly useful where access to the land under the bridge is difficult. Also used for steel bridges.

bascule – a single- or double-leaf bridge usually over a waterway which can be pivoted about a horizontal axis to give a clear headroom for vessels to pass through.

bitumen – a by-product of distillation of crude petroleum oil.

box girder – a girder of rectangular or trapezoidal cross-section whose web and flanges are relatively thin compared with the space in the box.

bowstring girder – a girder with a straight bottom chord from which springs an arched top chord, the two connected by rigid stiffening members.

breast shot wheel – a water wheel which is supplied by water at about mid-height.

buck – the body of a post mill.

buttress dam – a development of the gravity dam with the downstream face supported by buttresses, reducing the amount of material necessary to resist the water pressure.

bye-wash – a channel which allows excess water to by-pass a lock.

cable-stayed bridge – a bridge whose deck is directly supported by a fan of cables from the towers.

cantilever – a beam not supported at its outer end.

cast iron – an iron-carbon alloy with impurities which preclude it being rolled or forged; it has to be poured in molten form into moulds of the required shape and size.

centering – a temporary structure to support an arch during building.

conduit – an artificial watercourse, either in pipe or open channel, to convey drinking water. Often used also for the fountain, pump or other outlet from which the water is drawn.

crowntree – a great transverse timber beam at the top of the post in a post mill which rotates the buck and the sails to face the wind.

cut and cover – a tunnel or part of a tunnel constructed by excavating a cutting to build it and then burying it; often used at the ends of a tunnel to reduce the amount of actual tunnelling required.

cutwater – a v-shaped upstream face of a bridge pier; designed to part the flow of water and prevent debris accumulating around the pier; sometimes provided also on the downstream face.

dentilation – ornamentation resembling teeth, used to decorate cornices.

dripmould – a projecting course of stone or brick designed to throw off rain.

edge rail – a rail without an upstanding flange as opposed to a plate rail (q.v.).

embankment dam – resists the water pressure by its weight. Can be of compacted earth or rockfill with a vertical impermeable central clay core to prevent seepage through the dam. This form is particularly suitable for wide flat valleys. Rockfill types can have an impermeable upstream face rather than a core.

Engineer – the engineer in charge of the project.

engineering brick – brick with greater crushing strength than common brick.

extrados – the exterior curve of an arch, measured on the top of the voussoirs.

falsework – a temporary structure to support the formwork (q.v.) for casting concrete.

formwork – (or shuttering), a temporary structure to contain wet concrete and form its finished shape until set and self-supporting.

gauge – the distance between the inner faces of the rails for edge rail track or the outer flanges for a plateway:
standard gauge – the track gauge of 4ft 8½in in general use in Britain;
broad gauge – a track gauge greater than standard, up to 7ft ¼in, used by Brunel;
narrow gauge – any gauge less than standard, usually around two feet.

girder – a beam formed by connecting a top and bottom flange with a solid vertical web.

gravity dam – constructed of masonry or concrete resisting the water pressure by its weight, but because of the greater mass of the material the downstream and upstream slopes can be quite steep. This form is suitable for narrower valleys with sound rock for a foundation.

groyne – a timber, steel or concrete wall built at right angles to the shore to prevent or reduce littoral drift.

historical periods:
> early medieval – A.D. 410 to 1066;
> medieval – 1066 to 1536
> post-medieval – 1537 to 1900
> modern – 1900 to present day

immersed tube – prefabricated units in steel or concrete laid in an excavated trench in a river bed, jointed and covered over to form a continuous tunnel.

impost – the top part of a pillar, column or wall which may be decorated or moulded and on which a vault or arch rests.

incrementally launched construction – a bridge is cast in short lengths on the bank and a section pushed out over the valley using hydraulic jacks. As one section is pushed out another is cast behind and stressed to the previous one before it itself is jacked outwards. Permanent and temporary support piers are constructed in advance in the valley. The process continues until the bridge deck is completed across the valley. The bridge is then finally stressed to its design load. Also used for steel bridges.

intrados – the inner curve of an arch, also known as the soffit.

keystone – the central voussoir, often decorated.

leading lights – two lights by which a vessel may be aligned for safe entry into a harbour, usually one inland at high level and one lower down.

lintel – a horizontal beam over an opening.

littoral drift – the movement of sand or shingle along a coastline by the action of tides striking the coast at an angle and scouring the beach material.

loads: dead load – the total weight of the bridge structure itself;
> **live load** – the weight of traffic crossing the bridge and loads from wind, snow etc.

locks: flash lock – a single gate in a river weir which can be opened to allow boats to pass through;
> **pound lock** – an enclosed chamber with gates at both ends for moving boats from a higher to a lower level and vice versa.

mass concrete – concrete without added steel reinforcement.

navigator or navvy – labourer employed to excavate a canal, later any general labourer.

oculus, oculi – a round window or opening.

O.D. – Ordnance Datum, the mean seal level at Newlyn, Cornwall, from which Ordnance Survey measures heights in Britain.

order – where bridges have two or more arch rings and one stands forward of the one below, the arch rings are said to be in one (or more) orders.

overshot wheel – a water wheel which is supplied by water at the highest point of the wheel and turns in the direction of the flow (see pitchback).

pavement – the main traffic-carrying structure of the road
> **flexible** – a pavement constructed of asphalt or tarmacadam, or stone or concrete blocks;
> **rigid** – a pavement of mass or reinforced concrete.

pediment – the triangular termination of the end of a building etc. over a portico. Similar to a gable but with a less acute angle at the top.

penstock – a valve controlling a flow of water in a large diameter pipe.

pierre perdue – quantities of stone tipped loose into water to find their own position and form a breakwater.

pitchback wheel – a water wheel fed at the top but turning in the opposite direction to the flow, more efficient than an overshot wheel (q.v.).

plate rail – a rail, usually 'L'-shaped, on which travelled flangeless-wheeled waggons of tramways and early railways, the vertical flange of the rail providing lateral guidance.

portal frame – a frame of two vertical members connected at the top by a horizontal member or two inclined members with rigid connections between them.

post mill – a windmill in which the whole of the upper part including the sails and machinery is housed in a timber building all of which rotates on a large vertical post to face the wind.

post-tensioned concrete – prestressed concrete in which the reinforcement is contained in ducts cast in the concrete and tensioned after the concrete has set by jacking the bars or cables against anchorages cast at each end of the concrete unit.

prestressed concrete – concrete containing steel bar or wire reinforcement that has been tensioned before the live load is imposed. By utilising the concrete more effectively than in conventional reinforced concrete, lighter member sections can be used for a given load, though the quality of materials and workmanship required is higher

reinforced concrete – concrete containing steel reinforcement, thus increasing its load-bearing capacity

rolling lift (Scherzer) – a type of bascule developed by William Scherzer in America in 1893. As well as lifting, it also rolls back at the pivot point. It had advantages over the standard bascule bridge as it allowed the bridge to span greater distances, providing greater clearance over the waterway when it was rolled back.

roll-on/roll-off ferry – A ship which is loaded and discharged by vehicles driving on and off via a ramp (abbrev. ro/ro).

side pond – a small reservoir at the side of a pound lock into which some of the lock water can be discharged or recovered to reduce water use at the lock.

side pound – a widened area on a canal, usually situated where the distance between successive locks is very short, in order to provide extra water storage space.

sluice – in dams a system to release water at times when the reservoir level is below the spillway so as to maintain flows in the river or stream below the dam site; in water courses a barrier that can be raised or lowered to control the flow in the channel.

smock mill – a windmill having a timber tower resting on a stone or brick base. The top of the tower (cap) containing the sails rotates.

spandrel – the triangular area between the arch and the deck of an arch bridge.

spillways – release water when the reservoirs are full.

squinch – a small arch formed across an angle of a building or bridge.

stanch, staunch – a flood gate or watertight barrier.

statute labour – the requirement of the 1555 Act for parishioners to work for a fixed number of days each year on road maintenance.

stench stack – a hollow column from the top of a sewer to some height above ground level to allow ventilation of the sewer.

stringcourse – a projecting course of masonry or brickwork, often framing an arch or below the parapet of a bridge.

summit canal – a canal which passes over high ground and falls in both directions from the summit.

suspension – in suspension bridges the deck is supported by hangers from a suspension cable supported by towers and anchored to a foundation behind them.

tarmacadam or tarmac – a mixture of stone and a binding and coating agent of tar for road surfacing, or of bitumen (bitmac).

tower mill – a windmill with a brick or stone tower. The top of the tower containing the sails rotates, the machinery in the tower remains stationary.

truss – a girder in which the web is formed of discrete vertical and/or inclined members. There are many different configurations.

tub boat – an unpowered canal boat of less than normal dimensions carrying a few tons; often towed in trains.

undershot wheel – a water wheel supplied with water at the bottom of the wheel.

valve tower – built into a dam or nearby for the stored water to be taken off into the distribution pipe network or aqueduct for transmission to the treatment plants.

voussoir – the individual shaped blocks forming the arch.

wallower – the main gear in a wind or water mill which converts the rotation in a vertical plane of the sail or wheel into rotation in a horizontal plane to drive the machinery.

windpump – a windmill where the machinery drives a scoop wheel or turbine to raise water.

wrought iron – an iron-carbon alloy with few impurities capable of being rolled or forged as plate or bar.

BIBLIOGRAPHY

Barton, Barry, *Water Towers of Britain* (2003)

Beaver, Patrick, *A History of Tunnels* (1972)

Binnie, G.M., *Early Dam Builders in Britain* (1987)

Blackwall, Anthony, *Historic Bridges of Shropshire* (1985)

Boucher, Cyril T.G., *James Brindley* (1968)

Bressey, C.H., *British Bridges* (1933)

Brooke, David, *William Mackenzie* (2004)

Christiansen, Rex, *The Railways of the West Midlands* (1973)

Crow, Alan, *Bridges on the River Wye* (1995)

Hadfield, Charles, *British Canals* (1966)

Hadfield, Charles, *The Canals of the West Midlands* (1985)

Hadfield, Charles and Skempton, A.W., *William Jessop, Engineer* (1979)

Helps, Sir Arthur, *The Life and Labours of Mr Brassey* (1872, reprint 1969)

Hindley, Geoffrey, *A History of Roads* (1971)

Hopkins, H.J., *A Span of Bridges* (1970)

Jackman, W.T., *The Development of Transport in Modern England*, 2 vols (1916)

Jervoise, E., *The Ancient Bridges of Wales & Western England* (1936)

Jervoise, E., *The Ancient Bridges of Mid-and Eastern England* (1932)

Langford, J. Ian, *The Staffordshire & Worcestershire Canal* (1974)

Lindsay, Jean, *The Trent & Mersey Canal* (1979)

Long, P.J. and Awdry, the Rev. R.W., *The Birmingham & Gloucester Railway* (1987)

McDermot, E.T., *History of the Great Western Railway*, 2 vols. (1931)

Morriss, Richard K., *The Canals of Shropshire* (1991)

Peel, J.H.B., *Along the Roman Roads of Britain* (1971)

Priestley, Joseph, *Navigable Rivers and Canals* (1831, reprint 1969)

Reader, W.J., *Macadam* (1980)

Rolt, L.T.C., *George & Robert Stephenson* (1960)

Rolt, L.T.C., *Narrow Boat* (1944)

Rolt, L.T.C., *Thomas Telford* (1958)

Russell, Ronald, *Lost Canals of England and Wales* (1971)

Smith, R.A.B. and Grigson, T.R., *The Design and Construction of Concrete Roads* (1946)

Starkie, David, *The Motorway Age* (1982)

Steel, Wilfred L., *The History of the London & North Western Railway* (1914)

Whishaw, Francis, *The Railways of Great Britain and Ireland* (1842, reprint)

155